Anne-Marie Sapsted is an experienced journalist writing for national newspapers such as the *Daily Telegraph*, the *Daily Mail*, *The Times* and *The Sunday Times* and for women's magazines. She is the author of three other health books. She specialises in health and medical issues and also writes on education. She is married to a journalist and lives in rural East Sussex with her three children. Though never herself the victim of an eating disorder, like most other women, she freely admits to having fallen prey to the whim of food and fashion. She has had first-hand experience of eating disorders with a very close friend.

Jacky Fleming is a best-selling cartoonist. Her books, *Be a Bloody Train Driver*, *Never Give Up*, *Falling in Love* and *Dear Katie* are published by Penguin.

Also by Anne-Marie Sapsted:

The *Woman* A–Z of Family Health
Looking For Me
Banish the Post-Baby Blues

NOT TO BE SCOFFED AT

How to overcome eating disorders

Anne-Marie Sapsted

HEADLINE

First published in 1995
by HEADLINE BOOK PUBLISHING

10 9 8 7 6 5 4 3 2 1

ISBN 0 7472 5052 9

Typeset by
Letterpart Limited, Reigate, Surrey

Printed and bound in Great Britain by
Cox & Wyman Ltd, Reading, Berks

HEADLINE BOOK PUBLISHING
A division of Hodder Headline PLC
338 Euston Road
London NW1 3BH

DON'T change your body
CHANGE THE RULES

Contents

CHAPTER 1

Dying to be Thin

You've picked this book off the shelf, though of course you don't have an eating disorder, so it doesn't really apply to you, does it? But are you being totally honest? Take a look at these five questions and give honest answers:

1. Have you ever tried to lose weight because you thought you were too fat, even though your weight was in the acceptable range for your height and age?
2. Have you ever felt guilty about eating food?
3. Do you look in the mirror at your naked self and wish you were thinner?
4. Have you ever bought a dress that was too small with the intention of dieting to get into it?
5. Have you ever resorted to eating to make yourself feel better when you were depressed?

If you answered 'no' to all these questions, then you are a rare creature indeed. For the experts say that 90 per cent of women diet at some time in their lives, that 80 per cent of all slimmers are women, and that half of all women – including girls as young as eight – are on a diet right now.

For those of us who honestly answered 'yes' to some or even all of the questions, we now know that we aren't alone.

1

Dieting is seen to be a good thing because we think it shows that we care for ourselves. But the reality is that most people who diet are already a perfectly acceptable weight, and in many cases could be described as thin. Dieting is now seen as a perfectly normal way of life.

When *Slimming* magazine asked its readers why they wanted to diet, only one of the five most common reasons given had anything to do with health; the other four generally speaking were to do with fashion. They were:

1. To look better   26%
2. For health   21%
3. To feel better   17%
4. To wear nice clothes   13%
5. To restore confidence   11%

We no longer have a sensible view of food. We have become obsessed not so much with the quality of the food we eat and whether we are eating a balanced diet, but with the quantity. We want to look like the models who strut the catwalks. The irony is that while most of them are a size 10, 8 or even 6, it's well known that eating disorders among models are common. Estimates suggest that from one in five to nearly half are suffering from an eating problem. According to insiders, if a group of models sit down for a meal together, it is not uncommon for them all to go to the loo together afterwards, to make themselves sick before the food can be digested. Model icons such as Margaux Hemingway have admitted that they became bulimic in their quest for the perfect figure. Closer to home, it still came as a shock – though many already suspected privately – that Princess Diana had an eating problem. According to one biography, she suffered from recurring bouts of bulimia.

2

Dr Bridget Dolan, a psychiatrist at St George's Hospital in London, which runs a clinic for eating disorders, says that women particularly are under extraordinary pressure to diet. 'A woman is judged first on her body's appearance. Self-esteem is therefore linked to body image.' And the prevailing, acceptable, desirable image is *thin*.

And as the girls we think of as beautiful get thinner, so there has been a corresponding rise in eating disorders like bulimia and anorexia, and among ever younger girls. It would be over-simplistic to say that the desire to be slim is the only cause of eating disorders, but it feeds and supports other neuroses such as the fear of growing up or the need for control, and these express themselves in forcing the body to submit to our will.

According to one doctor, there are 30,000 people with full-blown anorexia at any given time, and for one in ten the illness will prove fatal. A 1983 survey by the Department of Health found that around 5% of fourteen-year-old girls were trying to lose weight. More recent research done at King's College, London, revealed that in one average group of twelve and thirteen year olds, 22% of boys and almost 40% of girls expressed the desire to lose weight. Some 8% of boys and twice as many girls were actively changing their diet in a bid to translate this wish into reality. But obesity is rare in children and teenagers, so thousands of young people are dieting simply to conform to the current view of what is fashionable. In fact the incidence of eating disorders and people who are seriously underweight has now become a major health problem in this age group. It is particularly sad that the people most likely to suffer from an unhealthy obsession are those whose living depends on their looks or weight – the dancers, gymnasts, girls working in the media, models. These women have very high rates of eating disorders. It is tragic to think of the normal, healthy girls desperately trying to follow their lead.

FAT IS NOT A NICE WORD

There is absolutely no doubt about it, *fat* is not a nice word. It isn't just the opposite of thin – which is definitely not considered an extreme, and is in fact something to aspire to in the 1990s – it carries with it all sorts of unpleasant connotations. Slim is beautiful, shout all the mainstream magazines and newspapers, advertisements, films and television programmes. If you want people to think of you as fit, popular, happy, successful and sexy, you have to be slim. If you are overweight, the message goes on, you must be lazy, stupid, lacking in self-control and generally not a very nice person to know.

You think I'm exaggerating? Consider this fascinating research carried out in America among a group of children. They were asked to look at six drawings of children and rank them in order of appeal: one could be described as average or normal; one had a limb missing; one was in a wheelchair; one was wearing a leg brace and using crutches; one had a facial disfigurement; and one was just fat. Without exception, the children rated the fat child as the one they disliked the most.

Alongside this message, there is also our Western obsession with food. It is no longer simple nutrition, but something to be experienced, something to be enjoyed. Preparing food, sharing it and relishing it are all ways of showing we care, of demonstrating how much we love those we cook for and eat with. Food is no longer essential fuel, it has to be exciting and *fun*. Despite the fact that, technologically, we have developed to the stage where food can now be bought ready-prepared in a huge range of recipes, fast food and pre-packed meals are generally frowned on. It's only considered good food it you've made it all yourself from fresh ingredients. No wonder that these two conflicting messages

4

leave trails of people in their wake who are unable to reconcile them. Food becomes a problem and they develop eating disorders. A MORI survey carried out in July 1993 discovered that one in four women is so worried about food that she doesn't enjoy eating.

The current attitude to food has now brought us a long way from a sensible, organised diet. One cynic claimed that food can now be simply put into four categories:

1. Good for you, but tastes bad, e.g. brown rice, bran, skimmed milk, boiled fish.
2. Bad for you but tastes good, e.g. butter, bacon, just about any pudding.
3. Makes you fat and ugly, e.g. pork pies, cream cakes.
4. Eat it and die, e.g. chocolate, luxury ice-cream, anything with fresh cream in it.

At the turn of the century, Freud blamed attitudes to sex for the neuroses he saw in society, but we have now got to a stage where food rivals sex. We are obsessed with it. We blame it for all sorts of psychological problems such as delinquency in children, for the major health problems in adults from heart disease to cancer. Eating some foods is now portrayed as dangerous, even life-threatening. All this adds up to a distinctly unhealthy attitude to food.

THE URGE TO BE SLIM

Throughout history our ideas of what is physically attractive in women have see-sawed. In many ancient civilisations the ample female figure was seen as ideal, though the ancient Greeks introduced the idea of aesthetic perfection which

5

favoured a thinner figure. Rubens painted curvy, plump women who were considered at the time to be the epitome of desirability. The Victorians went for the hour-glass figure, going to extraordinary lengths to produce tiny waists: women were strapped into corsets so tight they would sometimes faint and frequently had attacks of 'the vapours'; some even had their lowest rib on each side removed to achieve a better shape. But thin came in with a vengeance in the 1920s, then in the 1930s the Duchess of Windsor uttered the immortal words that women could never be too thin or too rich. We've been trying to live up to that ever since. There was a brief flirtation with the voluptuous look in the 1950s with the well-endowed Jayne Mansfield, and there have been similar curvaceous icons such as Marilyn Monroe and Brigitte Bardot. It was Twiggy who heralded the real change, though, and now in the 1990s we have a new ideal: the flat-chested, gaunt, snake-hipped, super-thin Kate Moss, the epitome of the much hyped 'waif-look'.

Researchers in America recently carried out a survey of Miss America contestants and *Playboy* centrefold models. From 1959 to 1978 there was a consistent year-by-year decrease in body size and weight. Since then the rate of decrease has slowed, though it is still at present levelling off at something between 18 and 19% *below* the average expected weight for someone of the model's height and age. This brought the researchers to the conclusion that the models can't actually become any thinner without dying. Medically speaking, being 15% below the average expected body weight is one of the major criteria for a diagnosis of anorexia nervosa.

No wonder then, that women in particular have become obsessed with weight. Gallup Polls have shown that in 1950, 44% of women thought they were overweight. In 1973, the figure had risen to 55%, and by 1980 it had shot up to 70%. By 1990 eight out of ten women really believed that they were overweight. These findings have been repeated many times in different groupings of women. A study carried out in 1966 found that around 65% of secondary school girls were dissatisfied with their shape and wanted to lose weight. By 1977 a survey showed that 75% of college students were actively trying to limit the amount of food they ate.

Doctors estimate that in the developed world, up to one-third of men and women are overweight, but surveys show that double this number actually believe they are overweight. One American study looking at the women who joined slimming clubs found that only half the members could be medically described as overweight. The latest figures in Britain show that despite this relentless pressure to control weight, women are in fact getting bigger. In 1980, 8% of women, and 6% of men were obese. In 1991 the figure had risen to 16% of women and 13% of men. As many as half of British women may not fit the 'ideal' size 10 to 12. The average size of British women is in fact size 16.

A DREAM INDUSTRY

The dieting industry is now reckoned to be worth more than £1 billion a year with products ranging from dietary supplements and meal replacements sold in reputable shops, to pyramid-selling techniques by housewives making pocket money, through to the more outrageous claims on the fringes of the health market for products such as anti-fat capsules which are supposed to make unwanted flesh disappear overnight. The slimming industry, of course, claims that manufacturers' studies prove that many customers do

Between you and me — there's a LOT of money to be made from keeping women anxious

achieve a permanent weight loss. And they insist there is no link between slimming and eating disorders. According to a survey by the Consumers' Association in 1993 most of the thirteen brands of shakes, soups, biscuits and bars they tested were found to be expensive, high in fat and sugar, and could provide no evidence that they worked to help people sustain weight loss. The report also stated that the products often contained just as many calories as conventional snacks and could claim to be diet products in the sense that weight loss occurred only when nothing else was eaten.

In July 1994 Alice Mahon, Labour MP for Halifax, put before Parliament a Private Member's Bill demanding regulation of the slimming industry, the 'dream industry' as she describes it. You would have thought her efforts would have attracted sisterly support from all parties in the House. But no, even this stirred up controversy. Back-bencher Edwina Currie, for one, gave her short shrift. 'It's all very well for you,' she replied. 'Some of us are not naturally skinny.'

Mrs Mahon became concerned two years ago when the plight of two anorexic girls in her constituency was brought to her attention. She wanted to see all sides of the slimming industry regulated, and aimed to force slimming centres and products to display warnings against rapid weight loss. She planned to make books, tapes and videos point out that permanent weight loss is unlikely and cannot be guaranteed. And she wanted diets, slimming pills, potions and patches brought under the Medicines Act.

According to Tom Sanders, professor of nutrition at King's College, London, slimming may yield short-term results, but 96% of people regain weight within three years because they have been drawn into a cycle of diet and binge. He is concerned by the refusal to accept natural body shape. 'In Britain, food has replaced sex as the national neurosis,' he commented. 'The EC is attempting to bring in legislation to keep this sort of obsession at bay. Marilyn Monroe was a size 16 and that is the average size today.'

According to Dr Sanders and his co-author, Peter Bazalgette, in their book *You Don't Have to Diet*, dieting is the problem, not the solution.

'The diet industry works under the false premise that there's something wrong with the food we eat. We're encouraged to go on restrictive regimes which encourage even faddier diets. We're gullible and are lured by the slim, slender, trim images. Most diet books offer a short-term weight loss, but they do nothing to help us permanently. Rosemary Conley says: "You must never eat chocolate again." What a sentence! Food isn't something to be feared. If you want to lose weight, you must cut down on fat, but you don't have to cut it out. That's bad nutrition. We're saying, put the pleasure back into food.

'We have reached a stage at which a perfectly normal function – a highly pleasurable one, too – gives rise to mass neurosis. Eating is something to feel guilty about and it has become almost normal to be "on a diet".'

EXPOSING THE PERILS OF DIETING

At long last, though, someone is beginning to fight back. And what's more the message is being listened to and acted on. For what started as a personal struggle in Mary Evans Young's Oxfordshire home is now finding echoes all over the world. Two years ago, Mrs Evans Young founded an organisation called 'Diet Breakers', a sort of Alcoholics Anonymous for addicted dieters, and this year they held an International No Diet day. The aim of this day was to highlight the myths about dieting, to challenge the tyranny of thinness, and to expose the tricks of the dieting industry. There were rallies, plays, discussions up and down the country, and it was the same week in which Alice Mahon chose to present her early-day motion on 'the perils and futility of dieting'.

Mrs Evans Young is herself a reformed dieter. For fifteen years she swung between compulsive and controlled eating, so she knows what she's talking about. She is a management consultant, and now runs courses aimed at helping women to develop their management potential. Diet Breakers' ten-week programme called 'You Count, Calories Don't' is designed to teach people a more natural attitude to hunger and eating. People are helped to learn the difference between concern about their weight and low self-esteem. They are encouraged to adopt a more sensible lifestyle, to enjoy food, and to disassociate it from weight loss.

'Dieting is extremely stressful, encourages an unnatural

attitude to food and has precious little to do with health,' says Mrs Evans Young. 'It's all to do with trying to make ourselves attractive in a society where attractive equals acceptable. When women diet it puts their lives on hold. It is something silently running in their minds 24 hours a day. It causes mood swings, feelings of guilt, lack of concentration and thus affects decision-making.'

FAT CHANCE

Attitudes about the way people look affect the way we react to them. Research shows that people we describe as 'fat' are discriminated against in all walks of life. Fat children are teased at school, and fat women stand less chance of finding a job. While it is acceptable for comedians to be plump – Dawn French, Robbie Coltrane and American soap star, Roseanne Barr, for instance – fat people usually play villains these days. They're often portrayed as greedy, stupid, ugly and lazy, whereas they used to be jolly and kind, though a little thoughtless – Billy Bunter, Mr Pickwick or Falstaff.

But the shape of our bodies is dictated by our genes. It is now thought to be determined in the early stages of pregnancy and no matter what we do, nothing can change it.

1. *Ectomorphs* – skeleton determines their shape, usually tall and thin.
2. *Mesomorphs* – muscle determines their shape, usually powerfully built.
3. *Endomorphs* – fat determines their shape, usually rounded.

Women naturally carry more fat than men, and that fat is stored mainly in the bottom and thighs, hence the most common shape of women, pear-shaped. Men on the other hand have more muscle and less fat which they tend to store in the upper part of the body. Fat plays an important part in the production of the hormone oestrogen, and is essential in the maintenance of female characteristics – the development of breasts and the lack of hair on the face, arms and legs – and also for fertility. This is why when women lose a large amount of weight their periods cease, and why women athletes and dancers who work hard to achieve a slim, trim figure often suffer from a loss of periods. Oestrogen is also vital for women's good health. It is part of the process which protects women against heart disease and osteoporosis. Women become more at risk from these two major diseases as oestrogen levels fall during the menopause.

FAT AND HEALTH

Overweight is defined medically as being between 10 and 19% over the optimum weight for the individual's age, height and build. Obesity is defined as being over 20% above this weight. But does fat mean unhealthy? Reading all the information put out by the medical profession in recent years, you would think the answer to that is a resounding yes. But the picture is not so clear-cut. One American researcher pointed out that a lot of the research which compares the health of fat and thin people is done using fat people who have tried and are constantly trying to be thinner – i.e. they diet regularly. There have been few studies which use fat people and thin people who are both quite happy with their weight.

Studies show that fat people are much more likely to diet

than thin people – that's an obvious finding. But in fact being a little overweight by today's standards is actually better for you than being too thin. For example, people who diet suddenly after a heart attack may well be increasing their risk of another heart attack. Being fat is far more healthy for you than other lifestyle factors such as smoking. Of course, being seriously obese, so fat you can barely move about, is a serious hazard to health, and increases the chances of suffering from a variety of diseases, but being a little plump can be a positive benefit. Thin women, for example, are more at risk of giving birth prematurely to low-weight babies. They are more at risk of osteoporosis, and thin people generally are more at risk of cancer than fat people. As far as mental health is concerned, fat people have a lower suicide rate than thin people.

The greatest threat to health as far as weight is concerned

is constant weight fluctuation – often called yo-yo dieting –
where weight is lost, then put back on, then lost again and
put back on in a rapid cycle. These people have an increased
risk of heart disease. In fact one large study in America
showed that people who said they had lost weight in the
previous five years were more likely to die from coronary
heart disease than those whose weight had remained stable.

It is not being overweight which is bad for your health, but
dieting.

CHAPTER 2

A Mirror Image

When a man looks in the mirror, according to researchers, he will automatically subtract a pound or two, or even more, from what he sees in front of him. He's much more likely to be satisfied with what he sees. Women, on the other hand – and these are perfectly sensible, healthy women, not those suffering from eating disorders – add anything up to half a stone or more and, almost universally, don't like what they see.

Recent surveys show that more than one in three women would like to change their shape. The most common complaints are that their thighs or bottoms are too big. The success of diet books homing in on these particular insecurities is testimony to women's sensitivity about their shape. The lack of fashionable clothes for anyone over a size 14 is one often-repeated reason for their dissatisfaction. Remember that *Slimming* magazine survey? Some 13% of women, when asked why they wanted to lose weight, said that they wanted to be able to wear nice clothes. The way we look, the way we want others to see us, is very important, and there is constant pressure on women to look slim. We are encouraged at every turn to lose weight.

Men, on the other hand, have a different image to live up to. To them, money, power and success are much more important. For a man to be described as thin is almost hinting that he's weedy. It's most definitely not a compliment. Most men, particularly as they get older, seem to prefer the plump, well-fed look. Their weight is carried almost as a badge of success.

Obviously society's attitude to weight is not the sole cause of eating disorders – the picture is much more complicated than that – but it creates an atmosphere which affects the way we think about ourselves. The Princess of Wales, speaking to a conference on eating disorders in April 1993, explained it very well:

'The quest for perfection our society demands can leave the individual gasping for breath at every turn. This pressure inevitably extends to the way we look . . . . From the beginning of time the human race has had a deep and powerful relationship with food – if you eat you live, if you don't you die. Eating food has always been about survival, but also about caring for and nurturing the ones we love. However, with the added stresses of modern life, it has now become an expression of how we feel about ourselves and how we want others to feel about us.

'Eating disorders, whether anorexia or bulimia, show how individuals can turn the nourishment of the body into a painful attack on themselves, and they have at the core a far deeper problem than mere vanity.'

The Princess described the condition as a victim's 'shameful friend' and went on:

'By focusing their energies on controlling their bodies, they have found a refuge from having to face the more painful issues at the centre of their lives. A way of coping, albeit destructively and pointlessly, but a way of coping with a situation they were finding unbearable. An expression of how they felt about themselves and the life they were living.'

The Princess is not the only beautiful woman to admit to suffering from the same insecurities as everyone else, though in her case her confession filled acres of newsprint and headlines shouted from every newspaper. Andie Macdowell, star of the films *Green Card*, *Groundhog Day* and *Four Weddings and a Funeral*, has talked about her struggle with her weight and appearance: 'I have to have a flat stomach, perfect legs and skinny arms or I'll be considered fat. If I put on, say, twelve pounds, people will tell me that I am too fat. Would they do that to a man? Never.' When asked if she had ever suffered from an eating disorder, Macdowell was very frank: 'I was never anorexic, but I wanted to be bulimic. I tried to make myself throw up and I just could not. I stuck my fist down my throat and nothing happened. I would have been bulimic if I could have been.'

The British actress Jenny Seagrove confessed that she, too, had been bulimic, and that at one point she felt it would completely destroy her. Jane Fonda also spoke about her eating problems which started as a child at boarding school: 'I loved to eat, but I wanted to be thin. It wasn't long before I was bingeing and purging fifteen to twenty times a day.'

DIETING AS A WAY OF LIFE

Dieting then has become part of our culture. We have arrived at a situation where dieting is normal; women do it regardless of whether they need to or not. The assumption is made that it doesn't matter what you weigh, it would be better to weigh a little less for all sorts of reasons which have nothing to do with good health: it would make you look better, i.e. thinner; you'd be able to wear more fashionable clothes; you'd be more attractive to men . . . the excuses are endless. But as we now know, dieting more often than not leads to overeating. Let's look in detail at the reasons why.

Instead of eating because we are hungry, because we need a certain amount of food to enable our bodies to work efficiently, and because we have come to enjoy good food, we start to choose food according to a calorie-counting method or according to strange combinations which are supposed to help with weight control. As this is tightly connected to the level of our will-power at any particular time, food begins to be consumed according to our emotional state at the time. Women in particular tend to turn to food for comfort. If we feel sad or depressed, we reach for food. If we are lonely or unhappy, food is a prop. We have a row with our partner or a

bad day at the office and we go home and eat, not because we are hungry, but because sweets or chocolates make us feel better.

Just as everybody's moods go up and down, it is not surprising that 98% of successful dieters will regain the weight they lost, but research shows that they will also put on a little extra, and usually the pounds go back on in less time than it took to lose them. And, as we've shown before, it doesn't matter how many times this happens, we continue to blame ourselves. Then we move on to the next diet . . . and the next.

How Does the Dieting Start?

Mary had just been asked by her best friend to be a bridesmaid at her wedding and was really excited. They started looking at the wedding magazines together and discussing which styles they liked. They went into a couple of shops specialising in wedding clothes to try a few things on and see which they liked. The ones favoured by the bride were tight-fitting, slim-waisted, off the shoulder little numbers, but Mary felt she was not quite the right shape for these. Never mind. There were nine months to go before the wedding. Mary could go on a diet and lose a stone or so. Just think how much better she'd look.

Nicola was planning a holiday with her friend Claire. It would be their first holiday abroad without their parents, and they were really looking forward to it. They spent hours together poring over the brochures and eventually found somewhere they could afford. After booking the holiday it was down to the serious business of dieting so that they could fit into that itsy bitsy bikini and the little black sheath that was perfect for evenings out. Everyone diets before they go on holiday and have to expose all that flesh, don't they?

Julie had fallen in love for the first time – with the boy up the road who caught her bus home from school every night. He already had a girlfriend who was thin as a rake, dark and very pretty. Of course he would never look at Julie who still had a little bit of what her mother called 'puppy fat' hanging around. It was all very well for her mother, telling her she would soon be tall and slim and pretty, but she wanted to look that way now. There was no other way. She would have to go on a diet, and it would have to be quite harsh to show quick results.

Three very common situations, three very easy ways to fall into the dieting trap. How many of us can honestly say that we have never done the same? The thing is that there are so many different options: liquid diets, high-fibre diets, low-fat diets, low-protein diets, high-protein diets, low-carbohydrate, high-carbohydrate, single-food diets, food-combining diets, foods eaten in a particular sequence, meal-replacement diets . . . . The list is almost endless.

The average man needs about 2,300 calories a day, and the average woman around 2,000 calories. The daily diet will consist of something like forty different food items: a mixture of basic foods which are cereals and starchy foods, milk and dairy products, meat and fish, nuts and pulses and fruit and vegetables. We then tend to add sugar, salt and fat to our cooking to improve taste.

Clearly our bodies need energy to function, and the two main sources of fuel are fat and glucose. Most of the glucose is stored in the liver and muscles for use in emergencies, after hard exercise, for example. What happens is that our bodies take in the food, it mixes with oxygen we have breathed in, and is translated into energy which makes our bodies function. When we create more energy than we need, the body stores it in the form of fat for use not only as reserve fuel, but also as a protection for the body's delicate organs. The rate at which we use up the energy is dependent on body weight, age, sex and levels of physical activity. So, for example, someone who works on a farm is going to use up more energy than a receptionist who sits at a desk answering the phone all day. But two receptionists doing the same job are going to use up different amounts of energy if one of them walks home after work while the other always takes the bus.

The most recent surveys show that as a nation we are getting fatter, but that we are not necessarily eating more. In fact, the healthy eating message seems to be getting through. What we are not doing is taking enough exercise to use up the energy we have, so we are *storing* more fat. You don't get fat quickly, however. One big meal is not going to make all that much difference. In order to put on 1 kilo (2¼lb) of body fat, you would have to eat:

25 hamburgers
or
75 cans of fizzy drinks
or
54 pints of beer
or
3 half-pound packs of butter
or
37 big bars of chocolate
or
113 eggs
or
27 pints of milk
or
135 chocolate digestive biscuits.

THE DOWNWARD SPIRAL OF DIETING

For years everyone thought the key to dieting was to cut out carbohydrates – bread, potatoes, pasta etc. – but all that changed in 1983 when the Royal College of Physicians published a report on obesity. All the old dieting theories were officially declared wrong: the report actually recommended a diet which included plenty of unrefined carbohydrates such as brown bread, brown rice, pasta, potatoes and cereals. It was recommended for both dieters and non-dieters alike, and it has certainly had a strong influence, especially in the meat-eating statistics, which have declined demonstrably.

Another discovery made in America around the early 1980s concerned the value of exercise to the dieter. A team researching heart disease found that aerobic exercise – exercise during which the heart and lungs are made to work hard for regular periods of time – increased the metabolic rate for up to 24 hours afterwards. Further research showed that dieting actually has the reverse effect: it *slows* the metabolic rate. What's more, each time you go on another severe diet the metabolic rate slows very gradually even further. The body is anticipating famine, stores up reserves accordingly and prepares to work on fewer calories. The only way to avoid this is to take a less dramatic route, diet sensibly and exercise at the same time.

Not only does dieting fail to keep the weight off, it is a dangerous game. It can reduce the skin's elasticity, especially if your weight yo-yos up and down: a big weight loss can leave you with the sort of stretch marks usually associated with pregnancy. Many diets also cause a lack of protein and, after a few weeks, hair can begin to fall out. Weight lost during the early part of a diet is likely to be mainly fluid, then fat and eventually lean tissue which means muscles. But once muscle is lost, it is never regained. What replaces it is fat. So every time you diet and lose muscle tissue, then go back to your old pattern of eating, the body immediately stores more fat. No wonder most people end up getting fatter after every diet.

Another key to the way the body works is the hypothalamus, the point at which the nervous system and the endocrine system meet. It lies at the base of the brain, receiving messages from the brain and also monitoring the level of hormones in the blood. It manufactures these hormones, which are then stored and released by the pituitary gland, located close by. The hypothalamus is responsible for controlling body activity and instinctive behaviour, as well as having a regulating role: it affects sleep patterns, appetite, body temperature, and sexual function among other things. Basically the hypothalamus regulates the workings of the body. When you diet, the hypothalamus monitors blood flow so that when the blood sugar drops as it usually does, a signal is sent out to find food to restore the balance. But long periods of famine, or dieting, can lead the hypothalamus to conserve energy by stopping the search for food thereby cutting down the energy the blood can carry to the cells. This leads to side-effects which frequently affect dieters: they often find it difficult to concentrate, suffer from insomnia, become lethargic and lose interest in sex. And of course, as we have seen, once the dieting stops, the body rushes to compensate.

Those who do manage to keep their weight down after dieting are people who tightly control their eating on a permanent basis. But most of us find that, once off a diet, we give in to the body's craving to replenish supplies, and eat at least as much as, if not more than, we did before the diet started.

A letter published in *The Lancet* told the extraordinary story of a twenty-three-year-old model who had spent years dieting to keep her weight down so that she could carry on with her job. Eventually, she could resist the urge no longer and started to binge. At one sitting she ate liver, kidneys, steak, eggs, cheese, bread, mushrooms, carrots, cauliflower, peaches, pears, apples, bananas, plums, grapes and two glasses of milk. The amount of food was enormous, and led to a weight gain of nineteen pounds. The strain on her body was too much and she died. This is obviously an extreme case, but the uncontrollable need to binge is one which every dieter will know, and it is one of the most serious side-effects. What happens is that because the hypothalamus has been thrown out of balance, the natural switch-off point when the stomach is full is not triggered. Though the stomach is full, the overwhelming urge to eat continues. Aside from the psychological effects of bingeing, it is physically very uncomfortable and causes stomach cramps and diarrhoea.

Many bingers resort to laxatives and diuretics to rid themselves of the physical unpleasantness (never mind the weight), but misuse of these can lead to dehydration, loss of essential body salts and minerals, and even a decrease in blood volume which can then lead to a weak and rapid pulse, fever and a feeling of weakness. It is often accompanied by an unpleasant sensation of impending doom, and can lead to a fatal drop in blood pressure.

The other way out for many bingers is to make themselves sick. Again this can have all sorts of effects on the body including potassium deficiency, infections of the urinary tract, kidney problems, swollen salivary glands, tooth decay, muscle cramps, depression, loss of periods, infertility and epilepsy. Despite its dangers, many women and increasing numbers of men resort to this method of weight control because it works. If you regurgitate your food before the body has time to digest it, clearly you aren't going to put on weight. But neither are you going to absorb the vital nutrients which your body needs to stay fit and healthy.

Even the slow-loss diets must be repeated regularly to maintain that weight loss. Anyone who has ever dieted has got to the 'plateau' stage where no matter what you do, the weight loss slows to a standstill and, no matter how strict you are, the pounds cling desperately on. Because you are failing to satisfy the natural hunger pangs over a period of time, your body thinks it is starving and holds on to what it can.

GOING TO EXTREMES

The pursuit of thinness has become so desperate that women are not content with restricting their diets to lose the unwanted pounds, they have been persuaded to go even further and resort to the knife. Cosmetic surgery is big business and promises not only to improve on nature but to solve the weight problem. It might seem like the magic answer to many but, like any form of surgery, it also carries risks.

Liposuction is now the most popular cosmetic operation in America, a trend which is catching on in Britain too. This operation involves converting the fat into a liquefied form and then draining it off. It can be carried out on various parts of the body, the thighs being most common, but it can be done on the breasts. However it costs thousands of pounds – surgeons do not like to remove more than 2 kilos (4½lb) of fat at any one time – and can lead to pain, swelling and scarring if it is not carried out properly.

Oh do you like it?
I had some of the
bulkier secondary
organs removed

Mammoplasty or breast reduction is a technique which involves removing breast tissue and reshaping what is left, which necessitates removing and re-siting the nipples. Women who have undergone this procedure no longer have sensation in their nipples, and are unable to breast-feed. Again this is expensive and, like any other major surgery, carries inherent risks.

Then there is the tummy tuck, most popular with women who cannot get rid of sagging stomachs any other way after pregnancy. It is also commonly used to get rid of so-called middle-age spread. Excess skin and fat are cut away and the tummy is made flatter by permanently stitching the abdominal muscles up nice and tight. If you feel you're in need of a more drastic reduction in the stomach area, then there is an apronectomy. The surgeon will cut you horizontally and vertically, cut out the fat and stitch you up again. This is also a major and very expensive operation.

The intestinal bypass was a procedure developed in the 1960s and was highly effective, but it had to be abandoned because there was an unacceptable number of fatalities. Improvements in surgical techniques, and no doubt a demand for more efficient methods, mean that this operation is becoming more common again. It involves removing most of the intestines so that food simply cannot be absorbed. In the past it led to diarrhoea, malnutrition and frequent stomach upsets. One expert estimated that anyone undergoing this operation was nine times more likely to die than someone of comparable age and weight who had not had the surgery.

Stomach stapling has become one of the most popular methods used by cosmetic surgeons in recent years. There are different ways of doing this, but basically the stomach is made smaller, therefore reducing its capacity for food, by using a surgical staple gun. It sounds ideal, but unfortunately the body has a way of adapting to such attacks, and the stomach can stretch to regain its former capacity.

Alternatively, a balloon can be inserted into the stomach and then inflated. In theory this tricks the stomach into feeling it is full but in fact diet still has to be carefully watched. At best this works only temporarily. When it was originally developed in the States, the idea was that it would be used only in extreme cases of obesity, but it was eventually approved by the Government for use by anyone.

If all else fails, the last resort is jaw-wiring. The teeth are wired together so that it is impossible to chew, and food is given in liquid form. People who've had this done must always carry with them a pair of wire cutters, in case they choke. It is undoubtedly an effective way of restricting calorie intake, but many women who have been successful at losing weight with their jaws wired have failed once the wiring was removed: when it was left to them to control their eating, the weight would inevitably pile back on again.

One research unit found a way round this, though. Two doctors from the Clinical Research Centre at Harrow, Middlesex, published a paper in the *British Medical Journal* about how they had managed to maintain weight loss in previously jaw-wired patients. The answer appeared deceptively simple. A nylon cord had been tied round their waists and had the psychological effect of controlling their eating.

There is no doubt that some of these procedures are useful as an emergency measure in cases of real obesity which have become health- and even life-threatening. But every time, once the patients are left to themselves, the success of the treatment relies on individual control of their eating patterns. There have also been continued warnings from experts in the field that surgical procedures for weight loss carry with them the possibility of serious complications, and should not be used for cosmetic reasons. So why on earth do we do it?

CHAPTER 3

When Food Becomes an Obsession

For over a century medical journals have carried descriptions of people – mainly young women – who have put themselves on strict fasts, lost large amounts of weight, and have become ill as a result. The first detailed description of the condition we now know as anorexia nervosa appeared in the 1870s, when Sir William Withey Gull, physician to the Prince of Wales, wrote a paper on the subject. (The doctor also had a reputation for rescuing prostitutes, and recently historians have suspected that he could even have been the notorious Ripper.)

Although it is difficult to be certain about the incidence of eating disorders, doctors have estimated that some half a million people in this country suffer from an eating disorder of some description. This may not necessarily mean full-blown anorexia or bulimia, but less extreme variations between the two. The phrase commonly used for both disorders is 'the slimmers' disease', but that underplays the seriousness of these conditions. It's reckoned that up to 20% of women binge at least once a month and, as we've already seen, almost all women have dieted at some time in their lives.

Recent research at the Hospital for Sick Children, Great Ormond Street, has shown that the numbers of children aged eight to fourteen suffering from anorexia has increased more than ten-fold in the last decade, with between 3,000 and 5,000 young children believed to have a serious eating disorder. Another study carried out in seven private and two comprehensive schools in England showed that in the private schools one girl in every 100 was suffering from an eating disorder. It has undoubtedly become a major health problem in the young in the Western world.

WHAT IS ANOREXIA NERVOSA?

Anorexia nervosa literally means loss of appetite through nervousness. This is somewhat misleading, however, as sufferers do not necessarily lose their appetites. In 1970, Professor G.F.M. Russell of the Institute of Psychiatry in London outlined three main features of the condition:

1. A deliberate avoidance of foods which the sufferer believes to be fattening, which leads to a marked loss of body weight. Often, but not always, the sufferer makes herself vomit, or uses laxatives, or excessive exercise or other means of ensuring weight loss. The sufferer may also have bouts of over-eating.
2. A hormonal disorder which shows itself in a loss of periods.
3. The sufferer has an obsessive fear of gaining weight, talks about 'losing control' and not being able to stop eating, and so puts all her effort into trying to stay abnormally thin.

While most anorexics are girls in their late teens, as we've seen, there are also very young anorexics, as young as seven or eight and it can hit people later on. One extremely rare case reported in medical journals involved a woman of fifty-one. The usual picture is that it falls between the ages of puberty and the onset of the menopause.

So how does it start? Most teenage girls are concerned about their weight, indeed some research shows that teenagers who do not share this preoccupation are rather unusual. And, of course, slimming at this age is a pastime shared with friends and schoolmates. Even so, few girls will go on to develop anorexia itself, though a significant proportion develop a guilty, unnatural attitude to food at this early age. The fact that society itself seems obsessed with slimness is bound to have an effect. Another factor which appears to play a part is class. Although some researchers dispute this, most say anorexia is more common in comfortable, middle-class families. New research also indicates a genetic factor at work. Sufferers from anorexia may carry a gene that increases their chances of developing the disorder.

Dr Ulrike Schmidt, a psychiatrist, then working at the Maudsley Hospital in London, carried out a survey based on 203 women attending an eating disorder clinic at the hospital. She thinks that the genetic blueprint for anorexia nervosa may be triggered by a life event. Reporting her findings, Dr Schmidt said, 'If you have that particular vulnerability, then when something unpleasant happens to you in adult life, you respond to that by losing weight and it takes on a life of its own.'

By contrast, Dr Schmidt's research shows that the roots of the other eating disorder, bulimia, appear to be in traumatic childhood events, including physical abuse. Now working at St Mary's Hospital in west London, Dr Schmidt discovered that while 45% of bulimics had problems with their upbringing, only 20% of anorexics had difficult childhoods. Women with eating disorders had frequently been latchkey children, left to care for themselves and, in some cases, for their brothers and sisters. Some 30% of both anorexics and bulimics had suffered sexual abuse, which also leads to problems of self-image. In 10% of cases, this constituted serious and repeated abuse from close relatives.

While this research is significant, Dr Schmidt was at pains to emphasise at last year's winter meeting of the Royal College of Psychiatrists that these figures did not lessen the impact of the media pressure to be thin. She said, 'Without this cultural pressure there would not be these eating disorders . . . dieting is now so widespread, women see it as the answer to their unhappiness.'

The Beginnings of a Problem
But how does it start? Most of us find it a struggle to diet. Anyone who sets out to lose weight will usually begin by cutting out the foods which are thought to be especially fattening: cakes, bread, potatoes, biscuits etc. It often includes fried food and fatty meat. Most people find it a terrible struggle, and most of us will occasionally cheat or give up before we reach our goal weight.

The potential anorexic will usually find it easier to get to her goal weight. In fact, she will characteristically reach that easily and keep on going. In fact this ability to keep in control and to keep on going gives the anorexic a great sense of satisfaction. After that, in most cases, the body weight remains at something like 20–30% below average. It is only in extreme cases that the loss is never enough, and the sufferer goes on losing weight until she puts her life in danger.

But let's go back to the average anorexic. It is quite common for those around her to be unaware of quite how badly she has been affected by her illness. She may wear big, baggy jumpers and other loose-fitting clothes, so that although she is very thin, family and friends may not realise *how* thin. It's quite common for those close to an anorexic to report how shocked they were when they first saw the state of the girl. They often panic at the sight of a skeletal frame and insist on emergency medical attention, when the sufferer can have been anorexic for months or even years.

The usual pattern is that having reached the low weight, the average anorexic will still be obsessed with keeping her weight down through limiting her food intake. All foods considered fattening – usually all high carbohydrates – will be avoided, though she may eat large amounts of foods which she considers healthy and allowable. Her food choices may often be bizarre and, because of the limits she imposes, extremely unhealthy because of this. It's not unusual for anorexics to eat, for example, large numbers of carrots. Carrots are, indeed, a healthy food, but when eaten in quantity and with little else in the diet, they can have the

effect of turning the girl yellow, and thus are not healthy at all.

What to most of us is a chore – daily decisions about what to eat and drink – becomes an obsession for the anorexic. She will count calories ad infinitum, tiny portions of meat will be carefully prepared and cooked, she will agonise over the various properties of different varieties of lettuce. She will eat unpalatable foods, such as bran dry. She will pore over slimming magazines and articles on food and dieting any-where.

One way the anorexic can avoid detection for a long time is to happily prepare normal meals for others, while at the same time always finding excuses never to eat her share. She will usually eat alone, eat very little and often surround the eating with little rituals which cannot be disturbed. Most anorexics say they aren't hungry, and while some will actually lose their appetite as a consequence of their absti-nence, others will suffer a continual urge to eat. These are the ones who will, almost inevitably, give way from time to time. The problem is that when an anorexic loses control, she will often binge on sometimes huge amounts of food. It is then that she may decide self-control is not enough and resort to other means – for example, vomiting or taking laxatives.

The first time she makes herself sick may probably be because, having eaten so much more than usual, she feels bloated and uncomfortable from the sheer amount of food. She is probably also worried about the weight gain this implies. But once she has discovered that vomiting very effectively prevents the weight gain, it can become a means of controlling food intake in its own right. Many anorexics learn to vomit silently, and some can do so without even putting their fingers down their throats. This new method of weight control can mean a return to more normal eating habits. Two or three meals can now be eaten a day in the knowledge that the food can quickly be got rid of, a pattern which can be concealed far more effectively from friends and family. This control may be maintained for a while but it is difficult to maintain consistently, so control becomes erratic: the girl may put on some weight, leading to panic and a return to a drastic reduction in food intake. It seems that most anorexics eventually, inevitably, give in to their desire for food and the vomiting behaviour follows.

But as the bingeing becomes more uncontrolled, so behaviour becomes more abnormal and emotions see-saw wildly. The sufferer often finds herself in the grip of a 'must eat' frenzy. Some rush to the cupboards or the fridge, consuming everything and anything in sight; others go off to the supermarket, loading up their trolleys with cakes, ice-cream, chocolate and massive amounts of carbohydrate, the antithesis of their 'healthy, controlled diet'. Some steal food and others ferret in dustbins to appease their urge for food. These binges are carried out in secret and lead to feelings of extreme self-loathing and guilt. Vomiting gives a temporary reprieve.

Some anorexics also become obsessed with exercise and fitness. They bring to it the same determination and single-mindedness they do to their dieting. It is usually tied up with a strong belief that exercise will help burn up extra calories from the food that has been eaten. But restlessness and over-activity are also a physical result of her illness. There are a number of other physical changes brought about by maintaining such low body weight. Restricting food intake so forcefully inevitably leads to a slowing down of the body's metabolic rate, so the anorexic usually feels cold: her skin is cold to touch and she often has a bluish tinge to her skin. The layers of clothes she wears serve not only to camouflage her loss of weight, but also have a practical value – to try to keep her warm. Many anorexics become covered in fine, downy hair which may also be the body's response to that loss of heat.

While the anorexic may complain about abdominal pain related either to constipation or indigestion, these are fairly minor problems. The major changes caused by regular self-induced vomiting or laxative abuse are far more serious. When it is allowed to function normally the body works like a fine-tuned machine, with the digestive system extracting vital nutrients which allow the cells and the hormonal system to do their job. Continual vomiting and purging cause a loss of digestive juices. The kidneys cannot do their job properly without essential elements such as potassium. Epileptic fits are quite common in anorexics.

The Mental Effects of Starvation

Apart from these physical problems, the continual restriction of food intake and weight loss have very definite psychological effects. These are not always fully appreciated, but they go a long way towards explaining why anorexics are so difficult to treat successfully.

As the anorexic loses weight, so her mental processes are slowly but surely altered. She becomes gradually less able to think complex thoughts. Anyone who has lived with an anorexic will recognise this. She loses the ability to think in shades of grey: everything is seen in black and white, good and bad, right and wrong. There is nothing in between. Imaginative and creative thought is lost, and she finds complicated or challenging situations difficult to deal with. So, for example, social situations such as parties will be too much to cope with and will be increasingly avoided. Relationships are obviously affected and any area in which there was difficulty before her illness will be particularly fraught with problems. She will appear to be highly organised in every aspect of what she is doing and will be unreasonably upset if anything untoward happens to upset her schedule. And while she may deny she feels hungry – and in many cases this may in fact be true – she will be totally preoccupied with food. She will talk incessantly about it – about calorific values, about what she will eat at her next meal, about how it will be prepared.

Then, as weight continues to fall, the sufferer will find it increasingly difficult to concentrate and her memory will deteriorate. She will also have less control over body movements so will become clumsy and even accident-prone. Emotions are affected, becoming ever less strongly felt, as are sexual feelings and interest. Anorexics often talk about a sense of detachment, and are described by others as being aloof or superior.

Fasting to this extreme also produces a sense of euphoria, a high, a feeling of elation. This is caused by the body responding to the lack of food by releasing adrenalin into the bloodstream in order to mobilise the body's reserves. Some psychiatrists have now come to believe that anorexics can become addicted to the feelings that starvation causes. She also becomes hyperactive and, not sleeping well, will often get up early in the morning and go jogging. She will hear and see things more intensely, and become more and more wrapped up with these inner sensations.

WHAT IS BULIMIA?

While anorexia was recognised and written about over a century ago, bulimia seems to have emerged only in the last decade. But the first medical paper devoted to bulimia nervosa ('bulimia' means having the appetite of an ox) appeared in 1979, written by Professor Gerald Russell of the Royal Free Hospital, London. Even then it was considered to be a variation of anorexia. Although there is clearly a link between the two and anorexics frequently become bulimic, anorexia is by no means a prerequisite for bulimia. It was probably the Princess of Wales, whose speech to a London conference on eating disorders I have quoted in a previous chapter, who really brought the condition out into the open.

The medical definition of bulimia says that essential features are binge eating, which the sufferer knows to be abnormal, accompanied by a fear of being unable to control the eating, depression and self-loathing and guilt afterwards. Bulimia is not caused by anorexia, nor has it been linked to any other physical disorder.

Again there are criteria which have to be met in order to diagnose bulimia:

1. Recurrent episodes of binge eating which involve eating large quantities of food, rapidly and usually in less than two hours.
2. Three of these factors must also be present:
   a) During a binge the sufferer eats food which is easily digested and high in calories.
   b) The sufferer binges in secret.
   c) The binge is stopped because of stomach pains, the desire to sleep, self-induced vomiting, or because the binge is interrupted by someone else.
   d) The sufferer keeps trying to lose weight by resorting to strict diets, self-induced vomiting, laxatives or diuretics.
   e) Weight often see-saws because of the alternate diets and binges by more than ten pounds.

3. The sufferer knows that what she is doing is not normal and is afraid she will not be able to stop herself eating once she starts.
4. After binges, she feels depressed, guilty about her behaviour, and loathes herself for it.
5. The binges are not related to anorexia or any other physical condition.
6. There are at least two episodes of bingeing a week for at least three months.

But what are the differences between anorexia and bulimia? It is estimated that about half of anorexics become bulimics. Though bulimia does affect teenagers, it is more common in women between the ages of twenty and thirty-five and can develop at any time up to forty-five. Anorexics seem to be more likely to be middle-class, shy and introverted, while bulimia is common across the board and sufferers tend to be more extrovert. Anorexics systematically starve themselves to get to a goal weight, and usually look thin and starved, while the bulimic's weight see-saws around normal. Bulimia is therefore much easier to hide than anorexia.

In practical terms, the bulimic has periods of binge eating which involve eating very large quantities of food which are high in calories. Many then panic at the prospect of putting on a large amount of weight and look for a way of avoiding this. Usually sufferers will make themselves sick, getting rid of the food before the body has had time to absorb it. Others resort to large quantities of laxatives, but regular users come to realise that this has little effect on weight control. This is because most of the food is absorbed in the small intestine, while laxatives work on the large intestine, so it is already too late. But many bulimics giving themselves laxatives feel better afterwards, because they have got rid of the sensation of being bloated. So, even though the laxatives are having little or no effect on weight loss, they become part of the behaviour pattern.

Some bulimics use diuretics even though they are also ineffective. They may lead to an initial weight loss, because the body is shedding liquid, but as soon as a drink is taken the weight goes back on as the body absorbs the fluid.

Others resort to very strict dieting or become exercise fanatics.

However the majority resort to vomiting in secrecy, often with the tap running or the toilet flushing to disguise the noise. They may start by simply sticking their fingers down their throats, but many eventually learn to contract the diaphragm and stomach muscles until vomiting begins. Many will repeat the vomiting over and over again to try to ensure that they have got rid of all the food. Some drink large amounts of water to 'wash their stomachs out', others start a binge with a particular food, so that when it appears they know they have got rid of everything. Because the food is relatively undigested, the taste is not as unpleasant as natural vomiting, so the sufferer does not associate a particular food with the unpleasant experience as often happens with normal sickness.

The Physical Risks of Bulimia

The most commonly quoted risk to bulimics is the effect that repeated self-induced vomiting has on the teeth and gums. To begin with, most bulimics binge on sweet foods with the obvious risk of straightforward tooth and gum decay. But far more serious is the effect which regular vomiting has on the teeth because of the gastric acid which repeatedly fills the mouth. The enamel on the teeth is gradually destroyed, and the teeth then become more sensitive to hot and cold. As the teeth become worn down, so fillings which are not affected become more prominent. Bulimics often brush their teeth very strongly after vomiting in an effort to get rid of the smell. This helps rub the acid into the tooth enamel and can cause permanent damage. Dentists can often be the first to be aware that someone has a problem of this kind, and may often mention it to the sufferer.

Because a binge causes the salivary glands to work overtime, they too can become swollen and sore, and some bulimics look as if they are suffering from mumps. Mouth ulcers can appear. A sore throat is common, not only because the bulimic sticks their fingers down it, but because of the action of the stomach acid on the tissue. Some bulimics sound hoarse and become more susceptible to throat infections. Repeated vomiting can also damage the oesophagus, or cause a hiatus hernia, and it often leaves the bulimic aching and sore. Laxative abuse can cause soreness and itching, and a loss of bowel tone which in turn leads to constipation and the need for ever more laxatives.

Many bulimics have dry skin because of the loss of water, some have numb fingers and toes. Others find that their hair begins to fall out.

As we saw with anorexics, repeated vomiting has an effect on the body's self-balancing mechanisms, and interfering with this can cause numbness, pins and needles, low blood pressure, changes in the heart rhythm, kidney damage and epileptic fits. Doctors also estimate that 40% of bulimics will have irregular periods. In around one in five menstruation stops completely. As with anorexia, the body's metabolic rate is slowed because the food from the binge is given so little time to be absorbed, the body thinks it hasn't had any fuel at all.

Bulimia is thought to affect as many as 100,000 women but, because it is much easier to hide than anorexia, this could be an underestimate. Bulimics tend to be older than anorexics, though they are most often women in their early twenties who were overweight as children. It is supposed to be particularly common among career women, and experts feel it is on the increase.

WHY DOES IT HAPPEN?

A couple of years ago, the newspapers carried the story of Joanna Greenside, a twenty-five-year-old fitness instructor, who vanished from a leisure centre a few days before Christmas, launching a major search by police who feared she had been abducted and that her life was in danger. Some thirty-six hours later, Joanna turned up outside the centre in Hertfordshire and claimed she had been kidnapped and raped. She was in a dishevelled state, with mud on her clothes, and she appeared to be suffering from shock. Four days after that, she finally broke down and confessed to police that she suffered from an eating disorder, couldn't face the Christmas festivities, and had taken a train to Heathrow Airport where she wandered round the terminals, desperate to lose weight before the holiday eating and drinking began. During the subsequent court case – Joanna was charged with wasting police time – it emerged that though she had suffered first from anorexia, then from bulimia since her teens, she had managed to keep the extent of her problem secret not only from her doctor, but also her family and boyfriend. Joanna was eventually given a conditional discharge after the court heard that she was receiving help from an expert in eating disorders.

A few months before the case, bulimia had hit the headlines when it was described as a major cause of absenteeism from work and lost output costing industry billions of pounds every year. Writing in the official journal of the Institute of Personnel Management, Dr Eric Sigman, a consultant psychologist, pointed out that both bulimia and anorexia are 'not about food, but about fundamental unhappiness and turmoil'. They are responses to the problems of 'coping with life, avoiding painful issues, reacting to current stress and unresolved problems from the past'. Dr Sigman advised personnel managers that eating disorders are easier to overcome if detected in the early stages and suggested that it might be necessary to approach an employee or their colleague, to voice concern. But there should be no question of judgement or threatened job repercussion, he said.

The disease was often triggered by depression. Some people turn to alcohol or drugs when they are under stress, upset or depressed, but people with eating disorders focus on food. In response to the situation, personnel chiefs for several large companies have arranged for confidential counselling to be available in the workplace, in the same way as that given to alcoholics.

CONTROL OF EATING

It could well be that you've worked your way through this chapter and are sitting back thinking that it just doesn't apply to you. You can relax, you think, you haven't got a problem with food. Perhaps you haven't, but there is a whole range of behaviour around the edges of anorexia and bulimia which is not so obsessive or serious, but could be described as an eating disorder because it is neither normal nor healthy behaviour.

The control of eating begins early in everybody's life, just like toilet and other behaviour training. There are still those who believe, for example, that babies should not be fed on demand, but should be trained to feed at regular intervals. Because food is regularly available in our society and it is something we must all have, we have come to regulate it, to surround it with a whole set of rules and regulations. There is a time and a place to eat, an order in which we eat, a method to it, and because of our obsession with diets and dieting, we now have 'good' and 'bad' foods which must be limited.

But we aren't satisfied with these controls, are we? We start adding other little ones. How many of us can honestly say we don't? And how many of us can honestly say that we eat what we like, when we like? Who hasn't imposed some sort of control, or felt guilty because we've broken our own little rules?

CHAPTER 4

Have You Got a Problem with Food?

Dieting doesn't work. How often have we heard that message recently? But for some reason we just don't seem to believe it. Almost every new diet book that comes out ends up in the Top Ten Bestsellers' List. Every magazine or women's section in the newspaper regularly carries articles on diets and slimming. We keep on trying, and trying very hard every new gimmick that comes out. As MP Alice Mahon said when she tried to introduce her bill to regulate the slimming industry, 'It is a dream industry. You blame yourself when a product doesn't work and then move on to the next in the endless array.'

And that's the crux of the problem. We blame ourselves because we want to be slim. Somehow we hold out that goal as the answer to so many of our problems. If only we were thinner, then—

- it would make us and our partners happier in our relationship.
- we'd be able to cope better with the children and family.
- we'd be happier and more confident at work.
- we'd improve our chances of getting a better job.
- we'd be more attractive to men and find it easier to get a partner.
- life would just be so much better.

We might like to think that being thinner is the answer to all our problems. But the harsh fact is that it isn't. Ah, I can hear you all say, but at least it will make me feel happier about myself. If I think I'm looking better, then I'll feel better, not only about myself but about everything else as well. I think this might well be true. But, and this is the important one, if a diet makes you slimmer but only for a very short time while you stick rigidly to it, wouldn't the best course be to find a way of feeling good the whole time?

It could of course be that you're one of those people who are quite happy with the way you look and feel. Try these statements for size:

1. I tend to get a bit overweight every now and then, but I don't really mind.
2. I eat exactly what I like, when I like – I don't worry about food at all.
3. I've never been on a diet in my life.
4. I never feel guilty about what I eat or drink.
5. I'm what many people would call plump, but I really don't care.

If those statements apply to you, then you haven't got any sort of problem with food and have no need of any kind of help. You're also very lucky and a very rare person indeed. But back to the rest of us.

IS FOOD A PROBLEM WITH YOU?

Let's try and identify if we actually have what could be described as a problem with food. Try these questions.

Answer 'sometimes', 'often' or 'never' to each question and keep a note of your answers.

1. Are you often on a diet trying to lose weight?
2. Do you think your life would be better if only you could get down to your goal weight and stay there?
3. Do you try every new diet that comes out?
4. Are you constantly thinking about food?
5. Do you talk about food and your diet a lot?
6. Do you regularly count calories?
7. Do you regularly deny yourself your favourite foods because they are fattening?
8. Do you feel you have to finish every last morsel on your plate?
9. If you start something like a bar of chocolate or a packet of sweets, do you always finish it in one go?
10. Do you buy food to eat when you are alone?
11. Have you ever binged?
12. Have you ever made yourself sick after a meal?
13. Have you ever used laxatives or other drugs to try and lose weight?
14. Do you ever eat when you aren't actually hungry?
15. Do you feel you have good days and bad days with food?
16. Do you worry sometimes that if you start eating you won't be able to stop?
17. Do you often feel guilty about the food you eat?
18. Do you find it difficult to eat in company?
19. Have you ever avoided a social occasion because of worries about the food?
20. Do you eat 'properly' in front of other people, and then eat what you really want to when you are on your own?

21. Do you tend to finish off food that other people have left rather than throw it away and let it go to waste?
22. If you're feeling depressed or fed up, do you turn to food as a consolation?
23. When you're preparing a meal, do you tend to nibble constantly as you work?
24. Do you 'reward' yourself with food or titbits if you're doing something you don't really like?
25. If you're offered a choice of meals would you automatically work out first which was the least-fattening option?

If you've managed to answer 'never' to most of these questions, then you haven't got a problem. But if there are more than ten 'sometimes' creeping in, then you could well have a problem with food, or be creating one for yourself. If you are not seriously overweight, then there really is no harm in relaxing a little and forgetting about the calorie counting. If left to regulate itself, your natural appetite will not lead to either large weight gains or large weight losses. If you found that there were quite a few 'oftens' in your answers, then it's time to look honestly at your attitude to food and to consider whether you're either exaggerating its importance, or are using it as some sort of emotional crutch. If there are a lot of 'oftens', then you don't really need me to tell you what you already know: you have a problem with food which could well be described as an eating disorder.

CASE HISTORIES

Look at some of the other stories below and see if you recognise yourself.

Mary's Story
Mary works in public relations and is in her forties.

'I tried every new diet that came out and my weight
constantly see-sawed between eight to ten stone. One of
the things which kept me going was that every time I
got down to eight stone, people would tell me how great I
looked. But it was such a battle to stay there. I was
totally obsessed with food. I'd tell myself that I couldn't
do something I particularly wanted to do until I could
get in my size 12 clothes. Food ruled my life. When I first
stopped dieting, my weight rocketed to nearly twelve
stone. The trouble was my appetite had gone haywire
and I just wanted to eat all the time. But gradually, I
managed to get it under control and stopped feeling
hungry all the time. Then I started to lose weight
without even trying for the first time in my life. It was
such a wonderful feeling.'

Mary realised just in time that food was beginning to take
over her life. She would have answered 'sometimes' to quite
a few of the questions above. But it wasn't easy, as you will
see in later chapters. Once you have interfered with your
natural appetite, it takes time to re-establish sensible and
healthy eating patterns.

Petra's Story
Petra works in the fashion industry and is twenty-five years
old.

'I started to put on weight in my teens and just couldn't
seem to get rid of it. I tried to diet, but because I denied
myself my favourite foods which were all sweet things, I

couldn't resist the urge to binge every now and again. It invaded every part of my life. I turned down work at times when I felt I was really fat, I never went on holidays abroad with my friends because it meant going to the beach. I used to tell them I was allergic to the sun. I never went out to nightclubs either, because it meant wearing skimpy clothes. But all the time everyone thought I was really confident and I convinced all my friends that I just didn't like doing those sort of things, when really I would have loved to.'

Petra is probably like a lot of women who have problems with food, the tip of the estimated iceberg. She would probably have fallen into the second category, with quite a few 'oftens' in her answers. What happened to stop her unnatural eating pattern before she slid into full-scale bulimia was meeting someone who wanted to share with her all the things she had previously found she couldn't face. She also decided to change her job and get out of the fashion industry. In fact, the changes in her life meant that she found a whole new set of friends and interests. She feels that in many ways her problems were about growing up, and she gradually stopped her bulimic behaviour. She still finds herself feeling guilty about food now, she says, but these feelings are getting much less frequent.

Annabelle's Story
Annabelle, a housewife aged thirty-four, remembers the occasion which sparked off her real obsession with food.

'I'd always dieted on and off, but had always given up before I had reached the goal weight I set myself. I worried about it, but having children seemed to give me an excuse for staying a little overweight for a while. The real problem started the day I got an invitation to a reunion of girls I'd been at school with. I really wanted to go, but when I looked in the mirror, I saw this frumpy, fat housewife who couldn't fit into any of the nice clothes which still hung in the wardrobe from my days as a career girl in the City. I couldn't bear it. Since I had two months to go before the party I decided that this time I would diet properly. I picked out my favourite dress, which was two sizes smaller than I now took, and it became my goal to get into it. I still don't know how I did it, but I managed to wear it on the appointed day.

'All my old friends were terribly impressed at how good I looked, despite being a housewife with two toddlers at home. And my husband liked the new me, too, though he wasn't keen on my obsession with food around the house. After that success, of course, I couldn't stop. I felt that the slimmer I got the better things would be and the happier I would be. It didn't work that way and I ended up anorexic, my marriage nearly broke up and I almost lost my children because of it.'

Annabelle doesn't fit the usual picture of an anorexic. But when she finally went for help, and saw an expert in eating disorders, it turned out that she had had a problem with her weight as a teenager and had always suffered from low esteem, despite her successful career and her marriage and children. Having professional counselling this time around, she feels that she has finally overcome her tendency to use food whenever she faces a crisis in her life.

51

Jennifer's Story
Jennifer teaches French at an independent school and, at twenty-eight, has recently married.

'I suppose it started when I was at college. I was always a good cook and enjoyed it, so I was a magnet for people. I always had cakes and things newly baked in case anyone dropped in – and they always did – and I was famous for the dinners I cooked. But I always cooked too much, or made sure that I didn't give it all away, so that I would then finish it off myself after everyone had gone home. I told myself I couldn't waste it. Not surprisingly the weight began to pile on. I joined various groups and started dieting. I could do that well, too, sticking to very strict diets for anything up to five months at a time. It worked and I slimmed right down, but the first time I stopped the dieting and went back to eating, I couldn't believe how quickly the weight piled back on. Ever since I've been stuck in this diet/binge cycle, and to be honest I don't know how to get off.'

It is now more than five years since Jennifer faced up to the fact that she had an eating problem. 'I had been on a particularly successful diet and thought I looked wonderful. But nobody seemed to notice. Then the moment I started eating properly again, the weight piled back on. I felt awful. I went to my GP who referred me to a psychologist and although we couldn't pinpoint a particular reason for my obsession, it did help to talk about my feelings and preoccupation with food. She helped me to adopt a more sensible approach to food in general. I still look at myself and hate being fat – I wish I could be fat and happy but I can't – but I'm much less likely to resort to yet another crash diet now. I don't think I'm completely cured, because I'm not happy with the way I look, but I'm much more optimistic about things. It isn't the enormous problem it used to be.'

Anna's Story
Anna is a housewife, and every now and again she binges.

'This morning after I'd dropped the children off at school, I decided I ought to have some breakfast. So I made myself a bacon sandwich. There was some bacon left so I cooked it all and had two more bacon sandwiches. It's going to be one of those days – I know it, but I can't stop it. There was some of the children's cereal left, about a quarter of a packet, so I finished that off, too. All day I kept snacking and then it came to suppertime. Everyone else was eating, then I started too. Having cooked a meal for my husband and children, I had my share then finished everyone else's and what was left in the casserole dish. I made an excuse to nip round to the shop and spent £30 or so on biscuits, cakes and sweets. I know the girl in there and she gave me a funny look, but I made up some excuse about the children having some friends round for tea the following day. When I got home, it was almost impossible waiting for the children to go to bed. Then I told my husband I was going up to the spare room to sort out some of the mess in there. I suggested he went out to the pub. I couldn't wait to get on my own and just stuff my face until it hurt. I hate myself for doing it, and now I feel bloated and full. I just can't stop when this happens. Tomorrow I'll have to find a new diet and pay for what I've given in to today.'

Anna's story is very common. No one around her would know that she had a care in the world. To the rest of us, she is attractive, apparently outgoing and friendly, and has a busy life at home with her children. Her husband certainly has no idea that she binges. Anna has recently confided in a friend that she is worried about her problem with food. To her amazement, her friend admitted that she, too, had indulged in bingeing on occasions. Because there is very little available in the way of help in the area where they live, Anna and her friend are in the process of setting up a small self-help group.

Jo's Story
Jo, a housewife and mother of one, was thirty-four when she became anorexic. It happened after a prolonged period of family upset which culminated in her parents talking of divorce.

'The doctors told me that it was very unusual for someone of my age to become anorexic. But I realised later it was a response to what was happening between my parents. My illness made them stop arguing and focus on me. At the time I enjoyed all the attention I got, but it must have been hell for my husband. I had always had a problem with my weight and I used to go for weeks refusing to go out because I thought I was too fat. So I'd promise that once I'd got down to a particular weight and could fit into a certain dress, I'd go out for a meal with him. I'd eventually manage it and I remember sitting in restaurants eating almost nothing at all and looking round at all the other people there feeling very smug with myself. I used to think, "I bet they all wish they are as thin as me and could eat as little as me. I bet they envy me."

'I can't remember what made me stop, but again I was

sitting in a restaurant with my husband and I just ordered a proper meal and ate it. My husband couldn't believe it. The trouble is it didn't last long. I started bingeing after that. I remember my mother coming round to the house one day and finding me gorging on food out of the freezer. I wasn't even waiting for it to defrost properly. I was eating raw food. It was really disgusting. Now I think I'm better. I still have problems with my weight and every now and again have to diet a bit to control it. But I don't worry so much and I don't go to such extremes.'

These cases go from the very ordinary to the extreme, and illustrate the wide range of eating disorders and problems people have with food. If you are now beginning to admit to yourself that you, too, might have a problem, you're probably also feeling depressed and a little hopeless about it. You may well have spent most of your life trying to change your shape. You have probably dieted, given in to the urge to eat foods you consider 'bad', you may have made yourself sick, used laxatives, pills, anything and everything to attain this idealised image of yourself. You look around and see a society dominated by thin, beautiful, self-controlled women, and you see yourself as a failure.

Well, you're wrong. What you first of all have to accept is that you are not alone. It's likely that many of your friends have a problem, too. But like you, they are ashamed and unable to talk about it. This is a particularly lonely condition. You're probably closer than you realise to breaking out of this diet/binge cycle, this obsession with food. But you've been locked into this pattern for so long, you don't know how to begin to climb out of it. We've got some ideas which we hope will enable you to begin to help yourself.

• Think about being able to keep a box of your favourite chocolates in the cupboard, and only eating one or two at a time, and not feeling the need to hide away and eat the lot at one sitting.

• Think about having a terrible day. It started with a row with your partner, problems with the children which left them late for school and you late for work. You had a bad day at work and came home to more chaos with everyone expecting you to sort out their problems. But you are going to do just that, without the need to eat to get through it. You are just going to have an ordinary meal which will satisfy your appetite and not think about food for the rest of the evening.

• Think about how life would be if you didn't feel the need to diet all the time. Think about eating healthily, and even having three or four courses including pudding every now and again, and not feeling guilty and worrying that it will mean a strict diet for days to avoid those extra pounds.

All the people we've talked to in this chapter have managed to help themselves. Some were a lot worse than you, some not so bad, many the same. You can do it, too.

CHAPTER 5

Other Problems with Food

We have never had so much choice and availability of food as we have now in the Western world. Yet, still, we cannot simply enjoy our good fortune. Only fifty years ago, our struggle was to get enough food to survive, now there is plenty, and yet food is a battleground at every conceivable level.

Look around any restaurant and you will see people, particularly women, pushing food around their plates and not enjoying it. Yet food for many people has become a hobby, an absorbing interest, a passion. Magazines and newspapers all have their food columns, restaurant critics, cookery pages – they are considered a vital recipe for our enjoyment and entertainment. Food has now acquired a whole new meaning: it is about fashion and style. For women, being an adequate cook and able to feed a family is no longer enough. Supermarkets and bookshops are full of cookery books aimed at the housewife and home-maker, let alone the hostess and entertainer.

THE FOOD INDUSTRY

In the last twenty years or so, there has also been a revolution in the food we eat. The advent of so-called fast food has affected everyone's diet. And the range of foods available to us in supermarkets is now almost incredible. Not only that, but we now have electronic gadgets to make the preparation of food easier than ever before. We have in our cupboards the wherewithal, and in our kitchens the equipment, to turn out an appetising meal in minutes. The food industry spends millions of pounds every year persuading us to eat not only new and unusual foods, but the same, familiar foods which are constantly re-invented and re-packaged.

And then there are the snacks, every dieter's downfall. There is an argument that snacks form an important part of children's eating habits, helping them to maintain their needed high energy levels. But adults, too, will happily 'graze' on snack foods if they are available. How many of us find our way to the kitchen, the snack bar, or the sweet shop during the day for some little snack or other, not because we're hungry, but because we feel like something to eat?

As doctors have been pushing the healthy eating message

over the last decade or so, there is evidence that our attitude to food has changed. The majority of people, if questioned, know what this message means; they know something about a healthy diet and will express a preference for it. The advertisers have not been slow to catch on to this, so we are now offered a whole range of foods and drinks which are 'low-fat', 'low-sugar' or carrying the prefix 'diet', encouraging the belief that eating these foods will make us thin. On the other hand, there are the 'naughty-but-nice' foods which urge us to be 'naughty' and, by implication, guilty.

A TASTE FOR FOOD

We are born with instincts which tell us when we are hungry. It's well known that newborn babies actively prefer sweet tastes – breast milk is surprisingly sweet – and will show their disgust at bitter ones. We enjoy eating and from a very early age choose foods because we like the taste. Any mother who has weaned a baby on to solid foods can testify to the fact that babies and young children already have very definite ideas about what they do and don't like and what they will and won't eat.

The human body has sensors which trigger the feeling of hunger when either the stomach is empty or the blood sugar level becomes low. We respond to these by eating, either filling the stomach or raising the blood sugar level, and the signal changes. We describe it as feeling full. We don't want to eat any more. But these signals are quite complex. We need a *balanced* diet – a variety of foods – in order to get the nutrients we need. No one food, or one group of foods, no matter how much of it we eat, will give us all the nutrients we need to stay fit and healthy. If we eat a single food for a meal, our appetite will decrease the more we eat, whether or not we are full. But we will still have an appetite for other foods. Parents of young children will be familiar with this: children will often eat only part of their main meal and then say they have enough room for pudding. This explains the early popularity of diets such as the grapefruit diet. They appeared to work because they cut the calories and reduced the appetite, but they did nothing to satisfy the body's need for variety.

One research team looked at a range of different breakfast diets which, although containing the same amount of calories, protein and fibre, had different amounts of fat and carbohydrate. They discovered that while people struggled to get through a high-carbohydrate, low-fat breakfast (e.g. cereal, bread, low-fat spread, fruit juice, skimmed milk, scrambled egg and lean bacon), they ate all of the high-fat, low-carbohydrate breakfast much more easily (e.g. bacon, sausage, fried egg, fried bread, fried tomatoes, whole milk). The reason is that carbohydrates are absorbed into the bloodstream more speedily than fats, and so satisfy our appetites much more quickly. What happens is that though fat has more calories than carbohydrate, it takes longer to trigger the mechanism which tells us we are full.

THE DANGERS OF RESTRICTIVE DIETS

Research shows that the more we are exposed to food and drink, the more we are likely to eat and drink. The one group which consistently confounds all these statements is adolescents. Perversely, the availability and variety of food appear to have the opposite effect. They are the most likely group to restrict their diets, either because they claim to like only a small number of foods – often fast foods such as hamburgers, chips, pizza, crisps and cola – or because they take up dieting or a restrictive diet, such as vegetarianism. Very often the latter comes about, not because of any strong feelings about meat itself, but because of the vegetarian ideology. It is well known that teenage girls in particular are susceptible to the animal welfare arguments put forward by vegetarians.

A report published in early 1994 suggested that cancer rates and heart disease among committed vegetarians were lower than those among meat-eaters. It was disputed by some experts, but appeared to be good news on the face of it. But the problem is that while many teenagers have embraced the vegetarian ideal, they do not seem interested in the healthy eating message. It's boring. The result is that nutritionists are discovering adolescents with unbalanced diets particularly deficient in iron. What many are doing is existing on a diet of chips, pizza, crisps and cola, and ignoring the right sort of foods which will keep up their energy levels. Look closely at any group of teenage girls, and many will look pale and tired. It often has little to do with devotion to academic studies, more to do with early signs of iron-deficiency anaemia. They may already be feeling the warning signs: tiredness, lack of concentration, headaches and exhaustion.

The Importance of Iron
Iron is vital to the smooth workings of the body. It helps in the formation of haemoglobin which carries oxygen round the body. It is also essential for healthy muscles and is involved in some vital brain reactions. Adolescent girls need iron not only for these functions, but also, as they begin to menstruate, they need extra iron supplies to make up for the

blood loss. Studies carried out amongst this age group show that not only are they unaware of the importance of a balanced diet, but one survey in an affluent area of London found that one in five leaves home without breakfast, and that more than 16% of girls also skipped lunch.

The iron deficiency problem does not only affect girls. Another study carried out in a group of twelve to fourteen year olds at one London school discovered that along with one in ten girls, 3% of boys were anaemic. Added to this was the finding that 15% of both boys and girls had borderline iron reserves. Vegetarians and those dieting to lose weight are most at risk.

Generally, vegetarians and dieters carry three times the risk found in meat eaters and non-dieters, with around one in four showing signs of anaemia or low iron reserves. Iron found in red meat and meat products is more easily absorbed by the body than from any other food. It is already well known that iron is crucial for normal mental and physical development in the womb and during babyhood. Lack of sufficient iron in these early stages can lead to irreversible mental and physical impairment.

Describing the results of iron deficiency in adolescents is more complex. Studies have linked it to a greater susceptibility to infections, particularly in the chronically sick. Other studies show a link with poor academic performance and also with difficult or disruptive behaviour. The provision of iron supplements has been shown to improve all these problems. Indeed it could well be that thousands of schoolchildren are underperforming academically or behaving badly because of iron deficiency.

One study carried out by the nutrition and dietetics department at King's College, London, shows that girls who are iron-deficient and therefore anaemic recover less efficiently from exercise than their healthy contemporaries. One theory is that children with low iron reserves may compensate by reducing their activity level to avoid feeling tired and listless.

Iron deficiency over a period of time could also have implications for future health. It could mean susceptibility to bone disease, heart disease and being overweight. Long-term iron deficiency also means that women who then get pregnant risk their unborn baby's health and development. Iron tablets prescribed during pregnancy may come too late. Vital growth and development take part in the very early weeks of pregnancy, often before a woman realises she is pregnant.

Some scientists have said that iron deficiency is developing into a serious problem in the 1990s.

What to Do?

The richest sources of iron are red meat, poultry and oily fish. Green vegetables, bread, cereals, dried fruit, lentils, beans and eggs also contain iron. The problem is that though a food may be rich in iron, it may not be easily absorbed by the body, as in spinach, for example. One way round this is to take drinks which are high in vitamin C, which helps 'unlock' the iron in foods.

For adolescents particularly, a good breakfast is essential. Those who eat cereals four or more times a week get nearly a third more iron than those who eat cereals fewer than three times a week. Eating crisps, chips and fizzy drinks reduces the appetite for balanced iron-rich meals, and can lead to iron deficiency. Tea and coffee can also inhibit the absorption of iron.

Experts recommend that, because iron reserves are often so low among adolescent vegetarians, especially those living with a meat-eating family, supplements are advisable. But if you are really concerned that your teenage daughter is looking pale and tired and admits to feeling run down and lacking in energy, it would make sense to consult your family doctor. A simple blood test will be able to tell whether she is anaemic. Your doctor can also rule out other problems and can advise on a sensible, healthy diet if necessary.

CRAVINGS FOR FOOD

Nearly every woman – whether she has suffered from problems with food or not – gets a craving for sweet foods just before her period. Up until the beginning of this century, sugar was considered a luxury and out of the range of most people. We know well that sugar leads to tooth decay, but few of us understand quite how a large intake of refined sugar upsets the body's natural energy balance. A person who gets a large part of their daily calorie intake from sugar, not just in the form of sweets and biscuits and sugary drinks, but from the hidden sugars in processed food, may in fact be suffering from malnutrition.

Unrefined or natural sugar, such as that found in fruit, has distinct advantages over refined sugar. It is absorbed by the body more slowly and easily, whereas refined sugar often gives a sudden boost of neat energy to the system.

During pregnancy women often find that certain foods – especially coffee and fried or rich foods – are intolerable. On the other hand, some develop cravings for particular foods, especially sweet ones, but sometimes highly unusual things which are not foods at all, such as coal, soil or toothpaste. This condition is known as 'pica' and could be due to some nutritional deficiency, often iron or other minerals such as calcium, zinc or cobalt. Don't be tempted to diagnose your own problem and start taking vitamins or mineral supplements. Ask your doctor for advice first.

Both cravings and intolerance to food can also be caused by changes in the body's hormonal balance, and this can affect the taste buds. Within reason, these cravings can do no harm, but large helpings of puddings, fizzy drinks or ice-cream will make you put on a lot of weight. If you develop a craving to eat between meals, snacks should be slow-burning carbohydrates such as nuts, raisins, raw vegetables and dried or fresh fruit. If your diet is balanced and nourishing, your food cravings will be reduced.

FOOD ALLERGIES AND INTOLERANCES

Food allergies – reactions to the food we eat – have become very common, if controversial, in recent years. In fact a whole raft of alternative therapies, special diets, tests and foods have been developed to meet this apparent explosion of ill-health caused by the food we eat. Food has been blamed for many things, from simple symptoms such as rashes, blocked noses and headaches, to more complex things such as the way we behave or feel. There is no doubt that a number of conditions are related to an intolerance to particular foods, but food allergy is a term that the medical profession has on the whole become very wary of.

The term allergy was originally used to mean an unpleasant reaction to a foreign substance in the body, but in recent years, as our medical knowledge has improved, doctors now use it to describe a reaction caused by a breakdown in the body's immune system. The immune system is designed to detect, track down and destroy agents which infect and damage the body such as bacteria and viruses. The blood produces antibodies whose job is to attack the invaders. But an allergic reaction produces an abnormal type of antibody which reacts to specific foreign substances such as spores or pollen, or, as has been recently recognised, particular foods. The antibodies combined with the allergen produce allergic symptoms. In most cases, doctors can detect fairly easily what the allergen is, such as asthma triggered by dust or pollen. Food allergy has proved much more difficult mainly because it is not easy to detect the allergic reaction in the blood. This has led some doctors to doubt the existence of food allergies.

Scientists now know that foods contain chemicals which produce an abnormal reaction in some people but not in others. For example, caffeine found in tea, coffee, cola, cocoa and chocolate can produce symptoms of heartburn, palpitations and restlessness if taken in large quantities. Other substances such as histamine (found in cheese, beer, sausages and canned foods) and tyramine (found in red wine, cheese and brewer's yeast) are thought to trigger migraine in some people.

Researchers prefer to talk about food intolerance rather than food allergy, and studies have shown that some people do suffer from extreme reactions to particular foods. People sensitive to a food or drink often crave it and it may become very important to them. They feel the need to eat or drink it constantly, and feel better once they have the first few mouthfuls, or they may simply eat an abnormal amount of a particular food. Craving a particular food in this way can be an indication that you are sensitive to it.

Another indication of food sensitivity is feeling constantly hungry or thirsty, desires which cannot be satisfied by normal eating or drinking. Losing and gaining weight suddenly, sometimes overnight or during the day for no obvious reason can also be a sign of food intolerance. Another is mood swings. Food intolerance is difficult to recognise because a common symptom is the variability and unpredictability of symptoms which come and go or worsen or improve for no apparent reason. A common sign is a feeling of constant tiredness and of being generally unwell.

The first thing you should do if you suspect a food allergy or intolerance is to talk to your GP. Unfortunately some doctors are still hostile to the very idea of food causing health problems like this, and may not be very helpful. You may decide to consult an alternative practitioner or do something about it yourself. Books such as *The Allergy Diet* by Elizabeth Workman, Dr John Hunter and Dr Virginia Alun Jones (Optima) or *The Allergy Survival Guide* by Jane Houlton (Vermilion) may be helpful. If you decide to try to identify your own problem by means of an exclusion diet, never fast or go on a one- or two-food diet without medical supervision.

Asthma and Rhinitis
Difficulty in breathing and wheezing are the classic and well-known symptoms of asthma which may be accompanied by coughing at night. While substances such as dust and pollen are well-known causes of this condition, one trial discovered that some foods produced asthma attacks in nearly one-third of sufferers. Some people reacted so violently that they only had to smell the food for an attack to be triggered, though most actually had to *eat* the food.

Rhinitis is the medical term for a persistently runny or stuffed-up nose and though the symptoms are similar to a cold, they cannot be confused as, unlike a cold, they do not go away. The condition can in some cases be related to certain foods.

Coeliac Disease

About one person in every 2,000 or 3,000 people in this country is affected by coeliac disease. It occurs when gluten, a protein found in wheat, rye and barley, damages the lining of the small intestine, thus preventing food from being properly absorbed. This leads to problems including diarrhoea, loss of weight and, in children, a failure to grow. It can also lead to bone disease and anaemia. That the disease was caused by gluten was discovered by accident during the Second World War when Dutch children, deprived of wheat by the Germans, were forced to eat potatoes as a substitute. Children suffering from coeliac disease showed dramatic improvements.

Once coeliacs omit gluten from their diets – and there is a whole range of gluten-free products now commercially available – they are free of the unpleasant side-effects, but it is a diet they must stick to for life.

Eczema

Eczema is a common allergic reaction in both children and adults, causing a red, itchy rash most commonly seen on the insides of the elbows and knees. The rash comes and goes, but if scratched it can turn sore and then crust and scale. There is now very good evidence that in some people it can be caused by an intolerance to milk and eggs. The orange food dye tartrazine found in a wide range of drinks and foods can also be a cause of eczema. The condition is often treated with anti-histamine tablets and steroid creams. Chinese herbal remedies, although controversial, have shown some very good results in trials carried out at the Great Ormond Street Hospital for Sick Children and the Royal Free Hospital in London on very seriously affected children and adults.

Cow's Milk Allergy
This usually affects babies who are bottle- rather than breast-fed before the age of four months. It can cause colic, diarrhoea, eczema, vomiting and a runny nose. Alternative milk products can be given, but most babies seem to grow out of the symptoms by the time they are about two years old, and on solid foods.

Irritable Bowel Syndrome
This is a very common condition – sometimes called spastic colon – which affects twice as many women as men. Nearly one person in every three in this country will suffer from it at some time in their lives. The symptoms are severe abdominal pain, distension, with diarrhoea or a disturbed bowel habit. People often develop the condition after a bout of gastroenteritis or if they have taken several courses of antibiotics. It appears that sufferers have abnormal changes to the naturally occurring bacteria in their intestines. Because x-rays and blood tests often prove to be normal, some doctors believe that the condition is caused by psychological problems such as stress rather than physical problems. But one research team in Cambridge found that in a group of 182 sufferers, 122 patients treated by special diet lost their unpleasant symptoms.

Migraine
Again this is a common problem which affects more women than men. One woman in five between the ages of twenty and forty-five suffers from it, though why it should particularly affect women in this way is not yet known. Violent headaches usually affect only one side of the head at a time and are accompanied by sickness, dizziness and distortion of vision. The triggers include stress, excitement, tiredness,

lack of food and bright lights as well as foods such as chocolate, red wine, oranges and cheese.

Most people seem to have problems with a small number of foods, and it is worth trying to trace these particular intolerances. One research project at Great Ormond Street Hospital studied eighty-eight children suffering from migraine at least once a week. They found that eighty-two of them avoided headaches if they excluded certain foods from their diets.

Urticaria

A common condition, particularly of children, in which large red, itchy blotches appear on the skin. Some people also suffer from swollen lips and mouth. There are many factors involved, including light and heat, but food is very often implicated. Artificial dyes, additives and preservatives are common culprits, and yeast and cow's milk can also be involved.

CHAPTER 6

A Suitable Case for Treatment

Not all of those people suffering from eating disorders, even the most seriously ill cases, come to the attention of the medical profession. Some struggle alone to overcome their illness, and succeed; others seek help from therapists, priests, teachers, social workers or their friends and family.

In the case of anorexia, though, as the illness takes hold, it becomes obvious because of the sufferer's physical condition, and many will eventually come to the attention of a doctor, if only because friends and family themselves intervene. There is no simple answer, but what an anorexic clearly needs is to be persuaded to eat again, to give up the rigid control which has enabled her to starve herself. So first of all, the sufferer needs to put on weight so that the physical symptoms of starvation are relieved, and then the underlying problem must be sorted out so that she can happily return to a normal eating pattern. But how best to go about this?

In their fascinating and illuminating book, *Anorexia Nervosa and Bulimia: How to Help*, Marilyn Duke and Roger Slade point out that the way people approach the task of helping is influenced by the theories they hold about the condition. To simplify this, there are broadly two categories: those who believe that starvation and low weight in themselves produce serious psychological changes; and those who

71

ignore the physical and psychological effects of restricting food intake but work on the premise that there is a purpose behind the action of starvation, that there is some deeper meaning to the behaviour.

The most popular reason given for teenage anorexia is that in rejecting their naturally changing body shape, from formless child into curvy woman, anorexics are demonstrating a fear of growing up. Others regard it as a teenager's way of exercising control over her own life in a new grown-up world which seems completely beyond her control. Yet others see it as a response to unpleasant or unhappy episodes within the family.

It is very difficult to generalise about the sort of people who are likely to suffer from eating disorders, but it is possible to say that most anorexics are in their teens, are female, come from apparently happy middle-class homes, and tend to be reasonably intelligent. Nearly always, eating disorders begin with everyday dieting in the teenage years. Around one-third of anorexics were overweight before they started dieting, but why do some spiral out of control?

THE ANOREXIA STORY

We've already looked at the pressures from society to conform to the ideal thin shape. Alongside this, young women particularly are bombarded with information and products from the dieting industry about how to achieve this state. This pressure alone can be overwhelming for some sufferers.

'Control' is a word which is used a lot when talking about eating disorders. Anorexics are seeking total control over their bodies, the experts say. Most of us have dieted at one time or another and can remember that feeling of satisfaction when the scales tell you that you have been successful. For teenage girls, this kind of control over their bodies can be a response to the feeling that it is the only part of their lives over which they have any control at all. Anorexia is most often viewed as a retreat from the pressures of growing up. Because anorexia entails the loss of the physical characteristics of womanhood – breasts and periods – it is seen as a rejection of growing up.

This theory of anorexia being a young girl's bid to escape or avoid her burgeoning sexuality appears to be the most widely accepted. The idea is that as an adolescent, faced with a combination of social pressures in a changing world around her, and the personal pressures of growing up, the act of starving herself effectively switches off the whole worrying business. She returns to a stage of pre-puberty. Many experts believe that until this formal development has been re-activated, the underlying problems cannot be tackled, and therefore they emphasise the return to normal weight as a priority and will begin therapy by enforcing a weight gain.

Other anorexics find that because food is an important part of their family life, refusing it is a way of expressing their feelings of unhappiness about situations within the family. They feel it is the only way of making an impact on their family. For some the illness can be triggered by a single event such as parents divorcing, or by their leaving home to go to university.

Susie Orbach, feminist author of *Fat is a Feminist Issue* and *Hunger Strike*, explains the anorexic's refusal to accept food in terms of rejection of a world which has proved disappointing. On the other hand, in *Hunger Strike*, she says: 'For the compulsive eater the experience of eating, while fraught with anxiety, contains elements of soothing, and the impulse towards food is generally coupled with a desire to give to oneself, to quiet an upset, to make whole what is empty, to say what cannot be spoken. The anorectic can find no such momentary satisfaction.'

The therapists Marilyn Duke and Roger Slade have developed a whirlpool theory which makes sense of the various other theories. Their view is that the restriction of food intake leads to an inevitable restriction of a sufferer's ability to think, reason and make decisions. The sufferer, in contrast, believes she can think more clearly. Because, like all starving people, she is obsessed with food and eating, people who support her weight loss are *for* her, those who try to encourage her to eat in her view want to make her fat and are therefore *against* her. Running in tandem with this is the feeling that restricting her food intake means that she is in control. However, she is, of course, not truly in control.

The decision not to eat rebounds on the anorexic. The consequences of malnutrition affect the way she thinks about eating and the way she sees herself. As the anorexic eats less and less, so her thought processes become more one-track, and she becomes more determined not to eat. The further down this path she goes, the easier it is to stick to this decision. So she spirals downwards to the point of collapse.

Duke and Slade explain it thus:

'This whirlpool explains how it is that at any present moment self-starvers' decisions to control their food intake may be deliberate and reasoned, and yet how, over time, the dynamic relationship between the decisions they make and the changes these bring about draws them into a situation that runs away with them. The whirlpool effect shows how the decisions to continue starving and exercising are necessarily made from a different position from the decision to begin. In this lies the compulsive quality of the condition, the way that anorexics' choices are no longer entirely free. It also shows how it is that anorexia nervosa becomes life-threatening.'

A Genetic Link

The latest research shows that sufferers of anorexia nervosa may be born with a gene that increases their chance of developing the disorder. This possibility was first suggested in the early 1970s, but a team based at the Institute of Psychiatry in London recently found some corroborating evidence. The team recruited 246 pairs of twins, 99 of them identical, which means they shared the same genetic blue-print. Each was tested for their attitudes to eating using psychological profiling developed to investigate eating disorders. Analysis of the answers showed the presence of traits, such as unhappiness about appearance, that have been linked with anorexia. The team also found that dissatisfaction with body shape and a wish to be thin were more common among identical twins than ordinary twins. The team then developed a heritability ladder which ranged from zero (no genetic factor at all) to 100% (complete genetic determination). Body dissatisfaction came highest on the ladder, scoring 52%, indicating that genes are more important than environment in determining this trait. However other research indicates that, while there may indeed be a genetic factor at work, the disease is often triggered by a life event or trauma.

The Treatment

The problem doctors have faced with a girl who is seriously anorexic, and her understandably anxious parents, is how to treat. Intravenous feeding is one obvious answer to try and give some desperately needed nourishment. The major difficulty here is that, even though her life might be in danger, an anorexic who feels her control is being wrenched away from her might well refuse to cooperate.

In the past, it is no wonder that doctors turned to measures designed to reduce her resistance to treatment. Insulin therapy was one solution, designed to create an appetite, but with dangerous side-effects in sensitive patients. Electroconvulsive therapy (ECT) has also been explored. This is used in a variety of psychiatric conditions where patients display fixed patterns of thinking and acting, most commonly in severe cases of depression. But unless the eating disorder is linked to depression, there is no reason to use it. Surgery was even tried at one time, though this too showed few, if any, benefits.

Drug treatment is a popular way of trying to help anorexics who refuse to begin eating. Tranquillisers are used, either in a bid to overcome the patient's resistance, or with the patient's cooperation to try and reduce the overwhelming fears many sufferers have as weight begins to be regained. These have now also been shown to have unpleasant side-effects.

Some centres treating eating disorders adopted different strategies for dealing with the uncooperative patient. A common procedure was to isolate the anorexic, often confining her to a room by herself. She was not allowed any contact with family or friends, nor was she allowed things such as reading matter, television, even her own clothes or any of her possessions. These were considered privileges and she was allowed them gradually only in return for eating. Many anorexics who submitted to this regime gained weight, but returned to the anorexic behaviour as soon as they were released.

Although anorexia has been recognised, written about and treated by doctors for over a century, there is still controversy surrounding the handling of its victims. This dilemma was highlighted in May 1994 when twenty-seven-year-old Samantha Kendal had to resort to court action for the freedom to travel to Canada for treatment. She and her twin sister Michaela had entered into a bizarre slimming pact at the age of fourteen. When Michaela died, Samantha herself, at five feet, eight inches, weighed just four and a half stone, and was still losing weight. Samantha had tried everything over a number of years from tube-feeding to electro-shock treatment, drugs, counselling and private in-patient treatment paid for by the NHS. A special clinic in Canada offering psychotherapy was her only hope, she claimed.

Dr Chris Freeman, director of the Cullen Centre, a specialist eating disorders unit at the Royal Edinburgh Hospital, talked at the time about the problems facing those who treat anorexics. The first priority, he said, was to get the biochemical functions of the body back into balance. On the edge of starvation, sufferers are at risk of the lungs filling with fluid, making breathing difficult. At very low weights, the body can start to digest its own muscle which eventually leads to death by heart failure. In very severe cases, force-feeding by tube directly into the stomach is often the only way to save life, and in some cases patients are sectioned under the Mental Health Act to allow such treatment to be given. 'We emphasise a collaborative approach and as a start we encourage anorectics to take high-calorie drinks and nourishing fluids rather as you might take drugs three times a day,' explained Dr Freeman.

Some centres try to 'fatten up' anorexics with up to 5,000 calories a day, but many specialists are critical. 'We see the casualties of this approach here,' said Dr Freeman. 'The body simply cannot keep up, with the result that phosphate is dragged out of the cells and they break down.' This kind of rapid weight gain can also lead to severe pain in the anorexic, who feels she no longer has any control over her body or her life, and can lead to relapse into years of the condition. Some doctors feel that the physical effects of starvation on the body render anorexics incapable of responding to any kind of counselling or psychotherapy, but many others disagree. 'So long as the body is ticking over we would try to establish the roots of anorexia and plan the next stage of treatment,' said Dr Freeman. Some experts now believe that it is a mistake to aim at a return to full weight. Some sufferers may be better stabilising on 10 to 15% below their normal weight, enabling them to feel that they still have some control over their bodies, but able to get on with a relatively normal life.

Samantha Kendal's story had a happy ending. She returned to Britain in October 1994 after extensive counselling and therapy, apparently cured. She vowed then to pass on her experience to fellow sufferers as a counsellor.

THE BULIMIA STORY

In the same way as certain traits crop up regularly in anorexia sufferers, so bulimics have a tendency to conform to a pattern. The most common example of this is that almost all bulimics suffer from a poor self-image. They often appear to be perfectionists, they are easily frustrated, and some also appear indecisive. We mentioned earlier that women in general overestimate their size when looking in a mirror. For those suffering from eating disorders, this phenomenon has been particularly noted. Sufferers not only believe that they are significantly fatter than they actually are, but they also set themselves target weights and sizes which are always going to be more difficult to achieve and which are considerably less than those of non-sufferers. One interesting British study in 1993 tried to examine the influence of fashionable women as portrayed in the media on bulimics. Several groups of women were shown pictures of models taken from fashion magazines and then asked to estimate their own size by comparison. The group with eating disorders gave estimates around 25% bigger than they really were. While this is only one such piece of research, it seems very likely that constant exposure to popular images of fashionably slim and attractive women can help to undermine the self-confidence of those with eating disorders.

Many bulimics will have suffered low self-esteem for a period of time before they succumb to bulimia. When asked to describe themselves, bulimics will often use words such as 'fat', 'ugly', 'useless', 'weak'. People who feel this way about themselves often feel negative about everything that happens to them. If something goes right, then it is despite their own efforts; if something goes wrong, that's much easier to explain, it's clearly their own fault. The Princess of Wales' well-documented speech, to a conference on eating disorders, highlighted this. She said that in her view the problem often dated back to childhood, and as such might be prevented.

Many bulimics find it difficult to wait for what they want. If a bulimic tries to do something, she expects to be able to do it properly straightaway. So if she decides she is going to diet and become thin, she wants immediate results. It's not surprising then, when feeling uncomfortable after a binge, that she seeks immediate relief by resorting to either laxatives or making herself sick, rather than allowing nature to take its course.

so I made it to seven stone

A bulimic will often set herself almost impossibly high standards as well. This applies to the whole of her life: in her academic life, she can never achieve enough; socially, she cannot accept that she is a valued member of a group; personally, she never feels she looks attractive. Part of this is the constant terror that people will find out about her secretive eating behaviour, and will then judge her in the same way she judges herself. She becomes ever more tense and afraid, and the only way to relieve this is to binge and then purge which brings a temporary release from her overwhelming fears.

From childhood, bulimics have often been reluctant to

make their own choices. They frequently make decisions based on what they think others, particularly their families, want them to do.

A group of American researchers discovered that bulimics often feel like this:

- I want everyone to think that I'm doing the right thing all the time.
- No one knows the real me; if they did they'd realise how weak and stupid I really am.
- When things don't work out the way I want them to, I panic because I don't feel in control.
- I should be in control of what's happening to me all the time.
- When things go wrong, it's my own fault.
- When things go right, it's not because of anything I've done.

A Link with Depression

We've already explored the pressures put on women by society to conform to the thin-is-beautiful image, but could there also be a *physical* cause for eating problems? Some researchers have put forward the theory that a single genetically based biochemical disorder could be responsible for both depression and bulimia: the two seem to be closely linked.

One research team has been concentrating on two particular chemicals, tryptophan and serotonin. Tryptophan is an amino acid essential to the body's functioning. Strict dieters have reported that they feel depressed or down in the dumps, and experiments have shown that they have lower than normal levels of tryptophan in their bloodstreams. When insulin is produced in response to eating, particularly carbohydrates, the levels of tryptophan increase.

Tryptophan's role is to act on the brain to release serotonin, also called 5HT, which not only eases feelings of hunger but also makes you feel happier. Other unrelated research has shown that abnormally low levels of 5HT seem to be present in a whole range of psychiatric problems, from depression and anxiety to suicide, aggression and alcoholism. It is known that bulimics are prone to all of these conditions. We will look at this in greater detail later, but research has shown that one group of anti-depressant drugs raises the blood levels of serotonin.

It has also been shown that the effect which a period of strict dieting followed by a binge has on the levels of tryptophan in the blood is different in men and women. Men seem far less affected, and this could be one explanation why bulimia affects more women than men. The menstrual cycle also affects the availability of serotonin, with less produced before a period than at other times. Perhaps so many women feel the need to eat more before a period starts in order to trigger production of serotonin. It is also well known that hormonal changes cause the blood sugar level to fall before a period, which could explain why so many women have cravings for sugary foods.

A 1994 issue of the *American Journal of Psychiatry* reports a Canadian study that links light therapy – used to combat seasonal affective disorder (SAD) – and bulimia. A control group of bulimics began to improve after half an hour of light therapy each day. The researchers also found that bulimia is as seasonal as SAD – bulimics binge and vomit more in the winter months, just as SAD sufferers become more depressed. This may be connected to levels of serotonin: lack of light dampens the effects of serotonin, making us feel hungrier, and levels of serotonin are highest in the summer and autumn anyway.

But other research, notably that of Dr Ulrike Schmidt, the

psychiatrist mentioned earlier, shows that other factors are more important. She found that bulimia has its roots in traumatic childhood events, including physical abuse. Her figures showed that two-thirds of women attending an eating disorders clinic at the Maudsley Hospital in London had been abused or neglected as children. These women were often 'home alone' children (45% of sufferers) with a history of particularly harsh parental control. In some cases, they had been made to eat dog food for trivial offences, had been locked in cellars, or were forbidden to bring friends home. One in four of these women had been subjected to physical abuse, and some 30% had suffered sexual abuse.

Returning to the Institute of Psychiatry genetic research and heritability ladder, in comparison to anorexia, bulimia does not have a significant genetic component. Bulimia has a heritability factor of only about 28%, reinforcing the view that outside factors are the main triggers.

CHAPTER 7

Men and Boys Too

Peter's problem first came to medical attention during a routine visit to his dentist. The damage to his teeth and gums was such that she began to question him about what could have caused the problems. He was very evasive, and clearly embarrassed, and she began to suspect that bulimia might be the answer. Eventually, he admitted that this was indeed the case, and the dentist persuaded Peter to talk to his GP. It turned out that Peter had suffered from bulimia since his early twenties. His wife had married him unaware of the problem, but it had gradually come to dominate their married life and had on several occasions brought the relationship to breaking point.

Peter refused to eat meals with his wife and their two children, something which obviously puzzled and upset the children. He would often get up in the night and raid the fridge or the food cupboards, and his wife would find almost anything edible had disappeared when she came down in the morning. On some occasions he would go out and buy several hamburgers or other fast food, bring it home, and sit alone consuming it all himself. He was very ashamed of his behaviour but felt he could do nothing to stop it.

Derek is in his twenties, and joined the self-help organisation Anorexic Aid. He says that his experience of anorexia did not involve dieting but was all about keeping his weight down through exercise, something which became an obsession. Another man, George, also in his twenties, was obsessed with exercising. He started weight-training while he was at university, and gradually it became more important than his academic work. He started to miss lectures, concentrating instead on his two-hours-a-day weights session in the gym. 'I would be livid if anything interfered with that,' he says. 'I became completely obsessed with muscle definition, with having no body fat, that I put myself on a ridiculous diet. I wouldn't eat any fats, sugars, salt, milk, caffeine or alcohol. I ate only bland food such as tuna and rice. I looked really muscular and fit, but just walking up the stairs made me breathless and exhausted.'

if I were thinner

I'd be thinner

NO RESPECTER OF GENDER

Although there have been few descriptions of male anorexics in medical literature, those there are tend to agree that, generally speaking, anorexic boys and men behave in very similar ways to female sufferers. Bulimia, too, is no respecter of gender. Singer Elton John has admitted to suffering from bulimia, and it's more than likely there are other show-business personalities hiding the condition. And while both men and women who suffer from eating disorders feel alone and isolated, men have the additional problem of feeling a little freakish. After all, they are suffering from something traditionally considered 'a woman's problem'.

Bulimia is thought to affect about one in 400 men, with the ratio of male to female sufferers changing over the past five or so years from fifty to one to thirty to one. So if you're reading this as a male sufferer, and are dismayed at what appears to be total concentration on women as the victims of eating disorders, you really are not alone. You face the same problems, though it might be a little more difficult to find the right sort of help. But all the self-help techniques discussed in this book will apply to you, too.

While anorexia is thought by some to strike boys at a younger age, bulimia is thought to affect men at a slightly later age than women. This could be explained by the fact that puberty usually starts slightly later in boys than it does girls. Like women, some groups of men seem to be more prone to bulimia than others: not only sportsmen, but male models, dancers, athletes, men for whom weight is important to what they do. There is evidence that homosexuality can be a contributing factor, though some experts deny this. It has also been found that a larger than expected number of bulimics have problems with drug or alcohol abuse, and men with bulimia are more likely to have been overweight before they became bulimic. But it seems that as for the condition itself, men suffer in much the same way as women. Their problem is doing something about it.

John's Story

It was twenty years before John plucked up enough courage to tackle his bulimia. It had begun in his teens when his weight soared to over fourteen stone. Completely lacking in self-confidence anyway, he thought that he would never have any success with girls unless he slimmed down. The problem was that he loved food. 'The answer I found was perfect. I ate what I liked and then went off alone and made myself sick. At eighteen I was around six stone and I did have a girlfriend, so I thought I looked good on it.'

His mother could not understand what was happening and, after medical tests could find nothing seriously wrong with him, John was persuaded to see a psychologist. It did little good. Over the next ten years, despite being married and having two children, there were two very serious episodes when John's weight was so low, his health was seriously affected. By the time he was thirty-five, John was also an alcoholic. Eventually he was referred to an in-patient unit at a hospital and underwent what he describes as 'a more modern approach to treatment', which involved psychotherapy. This enabled him to get to the root of his problems. In common with most women sufferers, he had a very poor self-image and felt very much out of control of his life. It seemed to be passing him by, yet he felt there was nothing he could do to take charge of it. Gradually he was helped to understand his problems.

EATING DISORDERS IN MEN

According to feminist writer and therapist Susie Orbach, in her book *Hunger Strike*, eating disorders provide a 'graphic picture of the internal experience of contemporary femininity'. Women suffering from the disorder are 'echoing or proclaiming in an extreme form the actions, fears, concerns, desires, hopes and wishes of women in general'. Anorexia is a woman's way of dealing with 'unmet emotional need, desire and authentic initiations. In each instance of anorexia one can observe the most brutal internal struggle directed at suppression of needs that originate from inside the woman.'

Orbach acknowledges that eating disorders are not now, though, the sole territory of women. Statistics are difficult to come by, but few doubt that there has been a significant rise in the incidence of male anorexia. So is this because men, too, are suffering an identity crisis?

A recent survey of teenagers showed that while 75% of girls were trying to control their weight, so also were 39% of the boys. Some researchers still say that anorexia and other eating disorders among boys and men are relatively rare, accounting for fewer than 2% of all cases. They reckon that figure has remained relatively steady over the last thirty years. But research done at Great Ormond Street Hospital for Sick Children indicates otherwise. Referrals have been going up, according to Dr Brian Lask, a psychiatrist at the hospital: 'In my view there is a real increase and my guess is that the actual incidence is between 15 and 20%.' A survey by the Hospital of GPs showed that they had a tendency to under-recognise anorexia in boys.

The pattern of eating disorders in men is not clear. Researchers at St George's Hospital in south London, which has a specialist eating disorders unit, conducted the first major study of the disorder in men in the late 1980s. They discovered that more men were going for help, but the team was not sure whether this was due to an increase in the actual incidence or simply because the problems of eating disorders for men are being more widely recognised.

Anorexia in men has been recognised for more than a century. But it is only in the last fifteen years or so that it has emerged as a clinical entity. This same time span has also seen an interesting emphasis on the male body as an object of scrutiny. Until very recently, it has been much more acceptable for men to be overweight, and male stars have been overweight as well as slim and trim. Robbie Coltrane, for example, is much admired for his role as the drinking, smoking, gambling, and very overweight psychologist Fitz in the ITV series, 'Cracker'.

But this is the exception rather than the rule. Women are now being encouraged to look at men in the same way as men look at women: as objects to be ogled or otherwise. There has been a rise in soft porn magazines for women, such as *Playgirl*. Pop stars are young, macho and fit, and are frequently photographed half-dressed. Gone are the pale, interesting, introspective looks of the 1960s or the wild, individual, wacky looks of the 1970s. Enter the Chippendales, a group of male strippers who enjoy phenomenal success with women-only groups, and who have spawned numerous copy-cat groups. Film stars, too, need more than good looks these days. They have to be able to deliver the action, too. Arnold Schwarzenegger and Sylvester Stallone, Mel Gibson and Kevin Costner are testimony to that: the all-action, muscle-bound hero is the new male role model. From the television advertisements for clothes and after-shave to the new interest in keeping fit and pumping iron, the message to young men is clear:

overweight and unfit is not attractive.

One doctor who was part of the St George's Hospital research team, said:

'Before our study, I felt there were a lot of ideas about male anorexia which were off the mark: the idea, for example, that anorexia was a typically female conflict about the female body; that men who suffered from it were confused about their gender; that they were more likely to be gay or much more disturbed, or before they suffered from the disorder, much fatter than females and that they had a worse prognosis.

'What we found was that anorexia was as "useful" for boys as girls, and that it does not require a particularly disturbed boy to develop it. The boys we see are not more likely to have been gay or disturbed or bizarre before onset of this disorder, or much fatter. We treat them exactly the same way as girls and they do about as well. The study shows that anorexia nervosa is not a female disorder but a universal one that affects more women than men for social reasons.'

WE ALL WANT TO BE HANDSOME

One problem is, of course, that an eating disorder in a male is not as immediately recognisable. Boys do not have the obvious symptom of lost periods, and their clothes do not show it up in quite the same way.

Bridget Dolan, a research therapist, and author of a study of eating disorders called 'Why Women?', believes that the number of men suffering from eating disorders will continue to rise as more and more men are being judged by external characteristics. While the standard notion of beauty in women is seen as thin, in men it is large, powerful and athletic. But this, too, can result in abnormal eating habits. It is thought that anorexia is particularly common in male joggers. And research among body builders in Sweden showed that many of them have symptoms of the disorder. Ms Dolan confirmed this view. 'In the sports world there are plenty of men with terrible eating problems – rowers, jockeys, in any sport that demands you keep to a certain weight. If you want to find men with eating disorders, just go into any gym on the Fulham Road.'

Her view is backed up by research carried out by a psychologist in London in 1993. Apparently six out of ten men believe that a change in body shape would make them healthier and more sexually attractive to women. Interestingly, the same questions put to women about their partners produced the result that nearly a third of women do not like their man's physique. The idea that body shape is an important part of sexual attraction for the male will undoubtedly mean that men, too, will become more prone to eating disorders.

But there are differences in the way dieting affects men. To begin with, dieting has been shown to affect the brain chemistry of men and women differently. During adolescence, whereas girls lay down body fat to give them their softer, rounded figures, boys tend to put on muscle. Girls don't always welcome this newfound 'puppy fat', while boys are generally rather pleased with their more muscular appearance. The metabolic rate of men is also higher, so it could well be that they find dieting easier. It is also true that as women get older, their metabolic rate slows, so they are physically going to find it more difficult to maintain a lower weight. This affects women in their fifties, around the time of the menopause. Men, meanwhile, generally maintain their metabolic rate. Another point is that thinness in women is seen as a positive attribute, while men who are too thin are viewed as weedy, or described as weaklings.

There is no doubt, though, that for most men the answers and the treatment for their problems will be the same as for their female counterparts. If you are a man with an eating disorder, follow the self-help advice we give in later chapters. Talk to someone about it, a friend or a family member, or try your family doctor. Contact one of the organisations which deal with eating disorders. They will not consider you a freak. You are one of a steadily growing number of men who are suffering.

CHAPTER 8

Where to Go for Help

There is no easy answer to the problem of eating disorders.

Unfortunately it is not like many other illnesses where you can pop along to the doctor, get a diagnosis, a prescription for some pills and off you go. Indeed, the doctor is often the last person that people suffering from eating disorders want to see.

But there are a variety of ways in which to get help. You might try self-help (see the next chapter), or you can opt for medical treatment involving drugs, psychotherapy, group therapy or counselling of some kind. You might want to go it alone, to involve your friends and family, to try a self-help group for support or go for medical assistance of some kind. Most people need some kind of support to get them through. You might want to confide in a friend or relative, or someone such as one of the counsellors available on the Eating Disorders Association helpline (see back of book for addresses and telephone numbers), or you might feel better talking to your GP. In most cases, it's up to you.

DOCTORS AND SPECIALISTS

If you are seriously ill and incapable of seeing that you need help, or refusing to accept it, then you could find that matters are taken out of your hands. These cases are few and far between, but it is as well for everyone involved to be aware that under Part II of the Mental Health Act 1983, it is possible to compulsorily admit sufferers to hospital in the interests of their own safety. If you want to know more about this it would be wise to consult the Act, but doctors alone cannot detain someone against their will. The difficulty is that patients admitted to hospital under these circumstances are even less likely to be cooperative, and it may also sour their dealings with the medical profession in the future. One recent study of those who had sought help in self-help groups in one health region discovered that only one in five of the group had any involvement with a doctor concerning her eating disorder. Many sufferers express the fear of being locked away in hospital and force-fed.

This is, of course, extremely worrying, but often understandable. The difficulty for the medical profession is that those who suffer from eating disorders often only come to a doctor's attention when they are seriously ill. In the case of anorexics, they may be seriously underweight and in a life-threatening situation, which leaves the doctor with no alternative but to take drastic action.

One answer is to go to your family doctor at an early stage. Most will be happy to help. The difficulty here is that there are still GPs whose attitude to young women whose periods have stopped is to tell them to go home, stop being silly, and start eating properly. If your GP refuses to take the problem seriously, then arrange to see another one on the practice, or ask to be referred to a specialist in eating disorders or to a counsellor.

When the Eating Disorders Association carried out a survey of how sufferers rated their GP's approach to the illness, almost half said they found their doctor was particularly helpful. While most GPs would not claim to be experts in the subject, the majority will probably do the best they can to find you the right sort of help. In fact a report by a group of specialists in eating disorders said that mild cases of the illness can be dealt with perfectly adequately by family doctors with the support of self-help groups and therapists. More severe problems, including the majority of bulimia cases, would be tackled by a specialist. This is like any other sort of illness: if it's mild, you can, with a little help from your doctor, cope with it yourself; if it becomes serious, you need the extra support of specialist help.

A survey in 1993 showed that there are only twenty-one specialist eating disorders units in the UK. There are some 200,000 serious sufferers, but only 1,500 places available at any one time. Clearly it is difficult, but there has been such an enormous amount of publicity on the subject in recent years, more and more people are becoming aware of the problem.

COUNSELLING

Counselling can be a help, particularly in mild cases or as a support to others as part of overall treatment. There is, though, little evidence that simply talking can solve the problem in the long term. Victims of eating disorders undoubtedly need specialist medical help, but counselling of some sort almost always forms an intrinsic part of treatment. Doctors can treat all the physical symptoms of the conditions, but until the sufferer can be helped to understand why she is resorting to this behaviour and learns other ways to deal with her problems, then there will never be a full recovery.

James le Fanu, writing in the *Daily Telegraph* following the Princess of Wales' impassioned speech to a conference on eating disorders in 1993, roundly condemned her view of the situation. He said that bulimia is a deep-seated psychiatric illness. In his view, 'the serious psychopathology of bulimia does not readily lend itself to the talking therapies which the Princess of Wales seems so keen on'. But if you feel that talking to a trained counsellor can help you, then go ahead. There are no hard and fast rules, and while it is not the answer in every case, it can be the right treatment for some.

In fact, in recent months the whole idea of psychotherapy and counselling has come under attack. This is not because the therapies themselves do not work, but because of their misuse by some of the unqualified people practising them. You are at risk if you approach someone privately to treat you. Do make sure they are properly qualified and if at all possible get a recommendation from someone you know and trust, and someone who works in this field, preferably within the NHS.

The therapies which are often used in treating eating disorders are as follows.

Cognitive Therapy
This works by helping people come to terms with their weight and size, recognising what their real shape and appearance are. It also looks at the sort of things which are likely to trigger binges or purges, and helps the sufferer to view these situations differently and to cope with them. Experts report that this approach to the problem has proved very effective particularly with bulimics, with around 90% of binge eaters improving. It takes time, often several months of treatment and it does not work for everyone, but so far it has proved successful in the majority of cases.

If fifteen years of dieting has only made you feel worse do you think there's a possibility it doesn't work?

Supportive Psychotherapy

This works by getting sufferers to talk about their problems, helping them through the crisis point when they are coming to terms with their condition. A good therapist will enable the patient to unburden herself of all her fears, especially the guilt which is such a large part of most eating disorders. The therapist will listen, can often make specific suggestions about how to change behaviour or cope with situations, and may even offer practical help. The idea is that you feel as if you are talking to a friend, but as you are talking to an expert, you will get far more out of it.

Behaviour Therapy

Traditionally, behaviour therapy is made up of two strands: the first is the concept of facing up to something you are afraid of, but under controlled and supportive conditions to help you cope with it: the second is to change your behaviour by offering reward and encouragement. Therapists will often use a combination of this and cognitive therapy.

Relaxation Therapy
This speaks for itself, and is something used in all manner of treatments for both physical and mental illnesses.

The most important point in all this is that anyone suffering from an eating disorder must want to get better and must be prepared to work with the therapist to overcome the problem. What they will help you to do is have an increased self-awareness, to be more self-confident, to learn better ways of coping with stress and with problems that crop up in your life, without always turning to food.

DRUG TREATMENT

Brain chemistry alters in women suffering from eating disorders. People suffering from bulimia, particularly, are often depressed as well. There has been a lot of research to try and find a drug treatment to help people suffering from all the various kinds of eating disorders, and a review of clinical trials showed that by and large anti-depressants did help in the treatment of women suffering from bulimia in the short term. Over long periods, though, this improvement was much less obvious. Alongside this were the unpleasant side-effects which included things like a dry mouth, constipation and dizziness, but most unfortunately also tended to lead to a slight weight gain. Obviously this is most unhelpful in treating eating disorders.

One drug has so far proved extremely helpful, though it

has had mixed publicity in recent months. Fluoxetine hydrochloride, more commonly known as Prozac, was introduced in the late 1980s, and is at present the only drug specifically licensed for the treatment of bulimia nervosa. A large-scale trial in America and Canada showed that it can have positive results for sufferers, and although there are side-effects, patients felt that the improvements they made were outweighed by the side-effects which include insomnia, nausea and tiredness.

Controversy surrounding the drug in America alleges that it can cause suicidal or violent behaviour, but despite trials this has not been proven. It could possibly have more to do with the publicity which has described it as a wonder-drug and the over-use which has followed in America. In Britain, this is not likely to happen at present as the drug is expensive, and doctors are constantly being urged to cut their prescription bills.

As yet, because it is such a new product, there are no long-term studies of its use. It has proved successful in helping patients to control their bingeing and purging, but it is not a miracle cure and should be used in conjunction with other therapies.

ALTERNATIVE THERAPIES

All sorts of claims have been made about alternative medicine, and indeed some of these may prove helpful, particularly acupuncture, homoeopathy and herbal remedies. But there is no real evidence – there have been no clinical trials – that they help in the treatment of eating disorders. But if you find that, for instance, aromatherapy helps you to feel relaxed and better able to cope with life and its problems, then use it. The same applies to a range of other complementary therapies. The only word of warning is that when consulting a therapist, do make sure that they are properly qualified and are registered with the appropriate body.

Acupuncture

This is one of the oldest therapies. It is a technique in which needles are used to puncture the skin at certain defined points to restore equilibrium to the body. It is based on the belief that there is a nervous connection between the organs inside the body and the outer surface of the skin. Therapists believe that when the body is unwell, the flow of the 'vital energy' of the body is blocked for some reason. When this is opened up by using needles, the body recovers. It is often used to treat conditions which involve pain, such as arthritis, but also addictions of various kinds. Some acupuncturists apply their techniques to virtually any condition presented to them by a sick or troubled patient.

Homoeopathy

The average library has more books on homoeopathy than any other branch of alternative medicine, and most high-street pharmacies now stock a small range of homoeopathic remedies. The therapy is based on the principle of 'like healing like': homoeopaths believe that a sick person's symptoms are signs of the body's battle against illness and they try to stimulate, rather than suppress, this reaction. The remedy given is one which in a healthy person would cause the symptoms. Homoeopathy came to Britain more than 130 years ago and its most famous supporters are the Royal Family. It is also available on the NHS, and many GPs are now trained in homoeopathy as well as traditional medicine.

Naturopathy

Naturopaths believe that illness is caused by bad living habits such as eating the wrong foods, too much stress and not having enough exercise. As a result of this, waste materials and bodily refuse build up and poison the system. The therapy is aimed at getting rid of these toxic accumulations by adapting to a healthier regime, including a wholesome diet, hydrotherapy, manipulation and counselling. Naturopaths believe that orthodox medicine only drives the symptoms underground, ready to return another time, because it does not remove their cause. Many health farms began with this therapy in mind.

Herbal Medicine

Primitive man is thought to have worked out which herbs helped him sleep, pepped him up, made his cuts heal faster, and cured his fever. This instinct, which animals still have, became folklore and, in its extreme, witchcraft. When modern drugs were first developed, many used the 'active ingredients' of plants, e.g. aspirin from willow bark. Herbalists use whole plants to provide what they regard as gentler, more balanced remedies for a wide range of conditions. Research in China, West Germany and Eastern countries where herbalism is widely practised shows that it is effective in treating a number of common disorders.

Other Complementary Therapies

• *The Alexander Technique* is a method of 'perfect posture' training, said to help with a number of painful disorders and stress. It is a sort of physiotherapy with relaxation built in.

• *Aromatherapy* is a combination of face and body massage with essential oils extracted from plants. Specific oils target specific parts of the body and particular ailments.

- *Bach Remedies* use plant essences to create substances which are aimed at correcting the balance in emotional states such as obsessiveness, fear or indecision.
- *Colour therapy* is the use of colours to produce beneficial or healing effects. This is a 'fringe' theory, based on the idea that the colour of our surroundings affects our emotions.
- *Hypnosis* can be very dangerous in the wrong hands. The experienced therapist can put someone into a trance and plug in to different levels of consciousness.
- *Reflexology* is a system of diagnosis and therapy in which the soles of the feet and sometimes palms of the hands are massaged.
- *Shiatsu* is a form of oriental massage where the fingers are used to exert pressure instead of needles. It was devised as a preventative therapy that would relieve fatigue and promote health.
- *T'ai-chi* consists of physical exercises to encourage the flow of the vital life force, or energy, found in the air we breathe and the food we eat, but which is also partly inherited.
- *Yoga* is not strictly an alternative therapy, but it uses a combination of mental and physical techniques to produce a feeling of well-being, self-control and mental tranquillity.

EVERYONE IS DIFFERENT

The most important thing to remember is that every case is different. Some sufferers undertake counselling or psycho-therapy, and find it isn't right for them. One woman who ran a telephone counselling service for people with eating disorders reports: 'I had callers already in therapy who were really upset because they could not come up with a reason

102

for their condition. They think they can't recover, which is wrong. I'm not altogether sure it is always helpful in every case. If you say to yourself that you were raped at ten and developed an eating disorder at twelve, then it gives you the excuse to carry on.'

It is a question of finding the therapy which works for you. Many people are turning to alternative therapies not just to treat their conditions, but as a way of learning to relax and get in touch with their bodies and the way they work. Until you try them out, you won't know which you might find helpful, and which you might find simply relaxing and enjoyable.

CHAPTER 9

Helping Yourself

The way you think, feel and behave so far as food and diet are concerned probably has its foundations in your childhood. Maybe you are bulimic or anorexic, or maybe you occasionally over-indulge and get out of control. It could be your response to emotional upsets, or simply something you do on days when you are lonely, seeking comfort in the biscuit tin or a large bar of chocolate. But if you are truly hooked into compulsive eating or dieting, then you can think of nothing else, only food, dieting and putting on or losing weight.

The first step on the road to overcoming your food problem is to decide whether you actually *have* a problem. Look back at the questionnaire in Chapter 4. How many of the issues raised in that do you feel honestly applied to you? Those people who can be easily diagnosed as anorexic or bulimic need professional help, but there are many thousands of people on the edge. If you think you have a problem with food, then the first thing you have to do is to accept that you need to make changes in your life, and that you are going to have to do it yourself. There is probably something in your life which is making you unhappy and focused in this obsessive way on food, and you probably believe that if only you could get to your goal weight and stay there, then somehow the rest of your life would be different, too.

The way you eat may well have something to do with the way you feel. It could be that you are eating so badly that your diet is affecting the way you feel. You may find that putting yourself back on a healthy, balanced diet makes you feel better, both emotionally and physically. But it's no good telling you to start eating properly. Changes must be made slowly.

The second step on your road to recovery is to accept that diets just don't work. No amount of pills, potions, patches, powders, drinks, or any other substitute for good food and sensible exercise is ever going to work. And no diet is going to solve your other problems: it won't make you feel less lonely, it won't bring you more friends, it won't make you more popular, it won't in the long run do you any good at all.

None of it is going to be easy, but it is the only way to get off the food/diet/weight treadmill.

KEEPING A DIARY

If you are a compulsive eater, you might find it helpful to keep a diary of your eating habits. This might sound peculiar, and you might feel that it will make you think about food even more than you already do, but if you get it properly organised it should help you discover the sort of situations which make you turn to food for comfort.

Be totally honest with yourself and record what you eat, when you eat, whether you resorted to laxatives or made yourself sick, and what happened during the day which went both well and badly. Set out your diary in sections, so that you can look back at it easily, and don't be afraid to write down how you felt at any one time. You will be amazed at how this will clarify things for you. And if you decide to seek help from a counsellor or therapist, then it will be of added help to them, too.

The next step is to get back to normal eating. You've probably read those words and are already worried. You're probably thinking that if you do that, then you'll never be able to stop yourself. But you can and you will. There will, at first, still be good days and bad days. It's most unlikely that everything will change overnight just because you have decided to do something about it. You might even fall back into your old ways and have a binge, or feel that you've over-eaten and starve yourself for a day. It is not the end of the world. All is not lost and you are not a failure.

Look back at the explanation about why diets fail. Your body has learned to cope with a binge/starve cycle for a long time; you have effectively been at war with your body. It's going to take your body a little while to adjust to the fact that food is becoming a regular item.

It would help considerably if the next thing you did was to throw away all calorie counters and weighing scales. Your priority from now on is to eat well. Calories don't count any more. If you can't bear to throw away the scales, then at least stop consulting them every day. Restrict it to once a week.

From now on, you are going to eat three meals a day, and have two or three snacks. To achieve this, you are going to sit down and plan your days. It doesn't mean you have to be doing something all the time, but work out the things that have to be done and fit around these the things that you want to do; even if it's reading a book, or watching a film on television, put it into your diary. What you are trying to do is to avoid stretches of time in which you haven't got anything

106

to do, or, conversely, days when you seem to be chasing your tail. At this point, it will help considerably if you do not put yourself under pressure.

TRIGGER FOODS

Many people with eating problems come to recognise that certain foods always seem to trigger a binge. They can't just take one biscuit from the packet, or one or two chocolates from the box, or one helping of ice-cream, it has to be the whole lot, and after that a whole lot more things as well. If you don't already know what triggers you – and it doesn't necessarily have to be something sweet and sickly – try and work out what it might be. For some people it can be something as innocuous as an apple, or dried fruit. We've all experienced the situation where you taste something like crisps, nuts or olives sitting in bowls at a party, and then carry on nibbling until they have all gone. Something which triggers a binge is a food which makes you feel you really can't stop eating anything and everything. It may not always be something you like, or it could even be something to which you have an allergy and which leaves you feeling not very well.

The only way to overcome this is to avoid that particular food altogether for the time being. Don't buy it if you can possibly help it, so that it is not at home as a constant temptation. If there is no way to avoid it, have other things around which aren't a trigger and which you know you can eat safely without the worry of spiralling out of control.

When it comes to eating:

- Eat in company if you possibly can.
- Try to concentrate on what you are eating. Don't be

distracted by television, or try to read at the same time.

• If you possibly can, don't stock up your food cupboards for a while. If you have a family, this might be difficult, but you can use excuses such as you are trying to use up food from the freezer so that you can defrost it and give it a proper clean-out. As far as your food cupboards are concerned, you can use very much the same excuse.

• Try and eat at regular times and plan your meals in advance.

• Try to keep out of the kitchen or any other place where food is kept as much as you can.

• Try to avoid big supermarkets for a while, and shop where your choice is more limited.

• Remember that you might suffer from food cravings in the days just before your period. This is perfectly normal, and almost all women feel the same way. So be prepared for it.

It would help you enormously if you could do two other things at the same time. Take up some form of regular exercise, even if it's only walking the dog a couple of times a day. Swimming would be good, and most leisure centres and swimming pools now have quiet times of the day when you can go along and plough up and down as many or as few times as you can manage without being bothered by children. Regular exercise helps to increase your metabolic rate.

You might decide that now is a good time to take up an exercise class. Try and make sure that the instructor has a qualification from the YMCA. That way you can be sure they know what they are doing and will only introduce routines which are safe and sensible. If you would like to exercise, but don't want to go out to a class, you could try a video at home. Again the YMCA have a range of videos to suit everyone; The Fitness Club – using the expertise of the

YMCA – has brought out three videos which are tailor-made to different groups. These are available from all good video stores.

Try to avoid alcohol if at all possible. Not only can it increase your cravings, but it can also get rid of your inhibitions and so reduce your self-control.

WHAT DO YOU DO IF YOU FEEL A BINGE COMING ON?

Don't panic for a start. Think of something you like doing, or that you know makes you feel better, and do that instead. You could try avoiding the problem by going out of the house for a walk, or pop round to see a friend. If you have to stay at home, then draw up a list of things you like doing and choose one of those. You could decide to phone a friend, or have a long, luxurious bath, anything which you think will help take your mind off food.

And if you really can't stop yourself, then don't go back to the laxatives and making yourself sick or going on a starvation diet the next day. Don't feel disgusted with yourself. One of the problems you are going to have to overcome in the long term is that you are too hard on yourself. And nobody is perfect. You must learn to allow yourself small lapses. This comment from a sufferer says it all:

'Bulimics in battling against their perfectionism always look for the perfect solution. They will curse me for saying that the only cure – the only cure for them, as for anybody else – is to grant themselves a period of imperfection. That means existing at something over their ideal weight and not killing themselves for it. It means recognising that being nine stone instead of eight is no reason not to go to the beach, apply for a new job or buy delicious undies.

'Banning the pleasures of life perpetuates the problem, because you never see yourself having fun, developing new interests or just looking gorgeous.'

So if you fail, it is not the end of the world. It is just being normal. Write about the experience in your diary and then go back to your new eating plan as if nothing had happened. You may do this several times, but every time you avoid a binge makes the next time that little bit easier. And if you do

I just ruined EVERYTHING
with 1 piece of chocolate

JF

manage to avoid one, then reward yourself, give yourself a treat. Buy yourself a book, go out with a friend, buy yourself some flowers, get your hair done or do something that you don't do very often. And don't argue that you can't afford it. Aren't you saving money by not bingeing in the first place?

TAKING CONTROL

Take it slowly and steadily and you will win in the end. If you are reading this book, then you are probably unhappy with the way you use food and would like to change. Half of you desperately wants to be different, to be 'normal', but the other half despairs of ever being able to manage it. The problem for you is that in common with everyone else suffering from an eating disorder, you don't like yourself: more than that, you are disgusted with yourself and your behaviour and – so far – your inability to 'pull yourself together', take control and get on with your life.

You may have realised that there are deep-seated problems in your life and that a preoccupation with food and weight has become your shield against these, or your reaction to unpleasant or what you consider to be threatening situations in your life. This is the same for both anorexics and bulimics, though they do opposite things: bulimics eat when they hurt; anorexics stop eating when they hurt. The big problem is that by *not* focusing on food, you must now suffer the feelings and emotions you were avoiding, and it's not easy. You are probably going to feel angry, sad and lonely; you are going to feel a longing for something you can't immediately identify, let alone satisfy.

The whole process will be much easier if you have support. The most obvious place to look for support is to your family.

111

But for many people with eating problems, the family may be part of the problem. I have avoided as far as possible looking at specific situations within relationships and families, because it is very easy to blame other people for our problems, particularly our parents, or more specifically our mothers. I feel strongly that this sort of examination is best done with a qualified therapist. One bulimic put it like this:

'Talking to a therapist did help me see things more clearly. It was a family crisis which set me off. My grandmother died suddenly and, though there were at the time lots of problems in the family and my parents were constantly rowing, everything suddenly focused in on this death. I had been in the middle of all their problems, but suddenly nobody seemed interested any more. I was no longer the centre of attention and was left to cope on my own. I couldn't deal with that at all. The psychologist suggested that the bulimia had been a response to suddenly finding myself alone with all that stress and upset. It's an interesting idea and it makes sense. But I can't say that it actually helped me get over my bulimia. I had to do that myself.'

Talking to people with eating disorders of all kinds, stories like that crop up time and time again. Just because you know what causes the problem, doesn't always make it any easier to control your obsession with food. That is up to you. You may find help within your family. They may be supportive and understanding, but sometimes they can be critical and unhelpful. But you might find your sister is understanding, or a friend. As statistics show that a huge proportion of women have problems with food and weight at some time or another, there is every chance that someone in your circle of friends or family will be very sympathetic and understanding. What you need is a shoulder to cry on, and no matter how disgusting you think your behaviour is, it's extremely unlikely she will share your view.

You should try to talk to your family doctor if you feel that he or she is approachable. If you have always got on well with him or her and felt that you could discuss problems, then don't be afraid to mention this one. You won't be the first patient with an eating disorder they have come across, and you may be surprised at their interest and understanding of your problem. If they can't help personally, then they will be able to put you in touch with a specialist who can. It is worth a try.

In the previous chapter I gave a little space to alternative remedies, but there are a whole range of these which can at the very least give you a better sense of well-being. This is something which can be particularly useful when you are struggling to get away from a preoccupation with weight. This is a time to forget for a while about how you look and to concentrate on how you *feel*. You have been very hard on yourself for a long time and now you need to relax and pamper yourself for a change. The better you feel about yourself, the easier it will be to begin to cope with your eating difficulties and the problems which may have caused them.

REDISCOVERING YOUR APPETITE

You have been abusing your body for so long that you have probably got completely out of touch with its real needs. You need to re-establish a real appetite and real ability to know when you are hungry. You need to get back in tune with

113

your body and its needs. You need to become healthy again. *The Good Health Handbook* by Dr Peter Mansfield (Grafton Books) might be a good place to start. Dr Mansfield is a practising GP who has also worked closely with alternative practitioners for over fifteen years. His is a fascinating book, sub-titled 'Help Yourself Get Better', which not only looks at a range of everyday illnesses and gives advice on how to cope with them yourself, but also looks at ways of enhancing the body's general well-being and natural defences against disease. His advice, which draws on alternative remedies alongside conventional medicine, is sensible and practical and will certainly put you on the road to taking control of your body.

One word of warning: you are now beginning to feel a little better and you probably have some idea of what you are aiming for. Don't fall into the trap of substituting one obsession for another – your obsession with food and weight for an obsession with health and fitness. You will simply be exchanging one set of problems for another. And we all know those health freaks whose whole life is ruled by considerations of whether everything they eat, drink, wear or do is going to affect their health. You are throwing away all rigid guidelines and settling down to being more kind and considerate to yourself.

CHAPTER 10

Spotting the Signs and Offering Help

Finding out that someone you care for suffers from an eating disorder can be very disturbing. Often those closest to a sufferer are the last to notice. Obviously it is not something which developed overnight, and it's probable that your daughter or wife, your son or husband started off trying to lose weight in the same way that thousands of people do every day, and that it only gradually became a problem.

It can also be the case that if it is your child who is suffering from an illness like this, you don't actually really want to acknowledge it. You may be reading this book in the hope that it will prove your deepest suspicions and fears wrong. And suddenly you are beginning to realise that lots of things fit into place and you are living with someone who is anorexic or bulimic, or has a problem with food.

Where anorexia is concerned, it is usually those nearest to the sufferer who first raise the possibility that there is a problem which needs to be dealt with. For bulimics, their problem is much easier to hide or at least disguise. They can go on for years without others being any the wiser. The problem is that with anorexia, the sufferer will more often than not be quite horrified at the very idea that there is anything wrong. She may be very happy with the way she is. After all she's in control and she wants to be thin. When first confronted, she will probably deny there is a problem and may be openly hostile to those who suggest it. As parents or those close to an anorexic, you need to approach the subject with warmth, gentleness and tact. Her response will go a long way to either confirming your suspicions or proving you wrong.

You have then got to work out what you are going to do about it. Hopefully you have a family doctor you can turn to for advice and support. This may well be your first port of call, for he or she can advise you of the things you should be looking for and help you with the next step. But supposing you haven't got this back-up. You may feel afraid of making a fool of yourself, of being seen as an over-protective, interfering parent. After all, isn't everything the fault of the parents these days? You will probably be feeling guilty, or a failure. Where have you gone wrong? Is it all your fault, especially as there does seem to be a link between eating disorders and family life? You may feel intensely disappointed. You may have had great ambitions for your child and he or she may have been doing very well, either academically or in sport or the arts, and suddenly all this is threatened. You may feel concerned that your doctor may be tempted to interfere in your family life. He may start asking awkward questions, he may want to intervene and take a course of action you feel is an over-reaction to what after all is only an eating problem. You can sort it out, you feel, within the family. There is no need for outside help.

If things haven't gone too far then you may well be able to help your child yourself. But there are situations where waiting and doing nothing in the hopes that the problem will sort itself out can be dangerous. Your child may even have said that she will sort out the problem herself. Is it safe to believe her and leave her to it?

There are some situations where it is not safe to either

believe that your daughter can help herself sufficiently, or where you really do need urgent medical help. If you discover that laxatives or any other form of self-treatments such as diuretics are being used frequently, or that the sufferer is making herself vomit on a regular basis, then you need medical help to assess the physical condition of your daughter. If she has dropped to a weight 15% below her average weight, then this, too, is an indication that medical intervention is needed. In very general terms, once the weight starts to fall below this level, there can very soon be medical complications. If there is a weight loss of 35% or more, then the condition may be life-threatening. If the weight has been lost slowly over a long period of time, it is less dangerous than if the weight has been lost quickly at the rate of several pounds a week. The body can cope better with slow change of this kind than it can with sudden weight loss. If her periods have stopped, and there is no other physical cause for this, then it is time to do something about it.

It could be that you noticed the condition some weeks ago, confronted your daughter and she agreed to do something about it. She may be telling you that things have changed, that she is eating more, but to you she looks no different, possibly even thinner. If this has been going on for three or four months, then you will have to intervene and seek help. The longer she is locked into this behaviour and these abnormal eating patterns, the more difficult it is going to be for her to change them.

BEGIN TALKING

With an anorexic, the first priority is address the threat to health from refusing to eat by beginning to work out how to start her eating. On the other hand, the approach you make to a bulimic might be slightly different because her health is not in immediate danger. Until your daughter or wife (or son or husband) has accepted that there is a problem, it's best not to approach her by talking about food or weight at all to begin with. If you suspect that she has a problem with food, it may well have been going on for a long time and it is something about which she feels deeply ashamed and disgusted. It is unlikely she has confided in you (although she might have if she's been reading this book, and that will make things so much easier), but you should begin by talking in more general terms to her about how she feels. Is she depressed, under a lot of stress, unhappy about something that's happening in her life?

But be gentle and take it very easily. If she refuses to talk about her problems and insists there is nothing wrong, wait a little while and try again. Be as gentle as you can. At this stage, you may feel out of your depth and in need of some help and support yourself. Try your family doctor, or contact a group such as the Eating Disorders Association who have lots of experience and will be able to advise you on how to proceed.

Once she begins to talk about her problems – and she may not yet admit that eating is one of them – but still seems reluctant to be completely open and frank with you, try suggesting that she get some outside help. If you have already spoken to your GP, you might suggest she does, too. If you speak to the GP first, there is no need for your daughter or wife to know that you have already discussed it. She may decide she is ready to go for more specialist help, to a counsellor or therapist. Don't feel rejected if she decides not to confide in you. She may feel more able to be open and honest with a stranger, and it will probably be better for everyone in the long run. At least she has decided to get help, and that is the important thing.

But supposing the sufferer refuses to admit there is a problem, or will not go for help? She is probably afraid of the course the treatment will take. She probably imagines that she will be made to eat, that she will lose control and that she will put on weight. You can help overcome these fears by showing her this book, or any other book on the subject. You could send for the excellent information which the Eating Disorders Association publishes (see the back of the book). Or she might prefer to talk anonymously to one of the Association's helplines.

If she starts to talk to you, then go very slowly and at her pace. Sometimes she may want to talk, at others she may not. Remember she hates herself for what she is doing. She is sure you will be absolutely disgusted and horrified if you know what she is doing, and she needs continual reassurance that you will support her whatever happens. If she begins some form of therapy, it is going to take a long time and she may well have lapses and threaten to stop. She is terrified of failing and she needs you to support her efforts, but only in the way that she wants you to.

It is going to be difficult for you too, but try to remember these points:

- Don't try and take over her life and reorganise it for her.
- Don't make any comments at all about her weight or how she looks, unless, of course, she has made an effort for you or there is some special occasion. Only make the sort of comments you would make if there were no problem.
- Don't make eating and mealtimes a big issue. Just try to be as normal and relaxed as possible and don't talk about the problem while you're eating.
- Don't comment on what she is eating, or try and check up on what she's been eating while you aren't there. And, whatever you do, don't be tempted to try and check if she's made herself vomit.
- If she has been taking laxatives or other pills, then discuss this with her and agree with her to get rid of them. Don't do this unilaterally without telling her.
- If there are particular foods which trigger her binges, and she will know what they are, try not to have them in the house. It will be easier for her, too, as we have discussed in another chapter, if you don't keep large quantities of food in your cupboards or fridge for a while. But again, talk to her about it, and see how she feels. She might prefer to shop every day for the food the family needs, or she might ask you to do it.
- If you know she has been on a binge, tell her, but don't be tempted to have a post-mortem unless she wants to. It's best to leave that to her counsellor or therapist.
- Reassure her all the time that you are on her side, that you are not disgusted with her, and tell her that in your opinion she is doing well. She is quite likely to be very difficult to live with as she begins to get over her problems.

She may be short-tempered, impatient, tearful and generally miserable, but it will be a great comfort for her to know that she is not alone.

• Don't let her eating disorder take over your life. You will be no good either to yourself or her, particularly if she refuses to face up to the problem, or if she refuses to get help.

• If she stops her therapy, then there may come a time when you must say exactly how you feel about the situation, too. Being considerate and supportive does not mean becoming a doormat. Your feelings and well-being are just as important as hers.

NEEDING SUPPORT: ANOREXICS

For anorexics, the approach to food will probably be different. To begin with she may not be able to do other than eat very little and often. But quite soon, it may help to be more organised about mealtimes. It is going to take a long time, and you may resent the fact that this problem has affected your family the way it has. Be prepared for the changes that will come about. She has to be back up to around 90% of her normal body weight and have held it there for around nine or ten months before her periods will begin again. You will also find that she may become susceptible to minor illnesses and infections. At low body weight, the system has not got sufficient reserves to allow itself the luxury of symptoms of an illness. So while the sufferer may, indeed, have been infected by something like a cold, the symptoms – a streaming nose and a fever – will not have been present.

Once she begins to look better and begins to approach a reasonable weight, it is very tempting to think that the problem is solved and that life can return to normal, especially for the sufferer. At around 85% of her normal body weight, she probably looks almost recovered and it is very tempting to start thinking again in terms of her education, or a new job or her social life. She is at great risk now. She still needs support from you and her therapist or counsellor, probably now more than ever. This can be the point at which anorexics become bulimic. The people around them seem to think they are cured, they feel they ought to be cured, yet they still feel out of control and powerless. Or she may react by starting to lose weight again. Help and therapy at this point are critical. She may now have lost the control over her food intake and body control, but she needs something to take its place. She feels completely empty and needs something with which to fill the void. While she was in the depths of her anorexia, she could see things clearly in black and white; now everything is different, she is not so sure any more and it makes her feel bad about herself and everything around her. One of the things she has felt very strongly is that she ought to be able to cope on her own, that she shouldn't need help. It is a long slow process to get over these problems and to begin to go back to a more normal way of life.

The signs of recovery will eventually come. A greater flexibility, less rigidity in the way she organises her life are a sign that things are beginning to get better. She will start to feel able to respond to others, to be more spontaneous. But it takes time. As one sufferer put it:

'I started to question the all-or-nothing approach to dieting. Eating more than my calories limit one meal-time would have meant rushing down to the gym for a long work-out in the afternoon and almost hourly checks on the scales, never mind the starving that would have to follow to balance it out. Sometimes I still have to kick myself into accepting that eating more than I intended for breakfast is not going to affect my meals for the rest of the day.'

While the sufferer may appear to be very much better, she may never return to completely normal eating habits. Fears about food and putting on weight are the very last things to fade. She may still worry about her shape and size, but as long as her life doesn't revolve around these concerns, then there is no need for those around her to worry either. It may take a long, long time, but all the research shows that most anorexics and bulimics recover.

AVOIDING EATING DISORDERS

Child psychologists say it is not uncommon these days to come across children at primary school who are obsessed with body shape, who count calories, talk about dieting and refuse to eat chips, ice-cream and cakes because they are fattening. There is no doubt that children, particularly little girls, see a lot of this behaviour on television, but what about at home? Could a mother's attitude to weight be passed on to her children?

Annette was first of all amazed, and then horrified, one morning when she watched her seven-year-old daughter Amanda getting ready for school. Amanda rushed ahead of her mother into the bathroom and leapt on the scales. 'Oh dear,' was all she said. Although the child was simply watching the numbers spin round, she was copying her mother's behaviour. This was something Annette did two or three times a day. It shocked Annette, a life-long dieter, whose own eating patterns were dictated by whatever diet she was on at the time. For her it was a sharp lesson in how she could pass on her own obsession to her children.

Dee Dawson who runs Rhodes Farm Clinic for eating disorders in north London is treating twenty-two children and young teenagers at any one time. She employs a three-month re-feeding programme in which her young patients are encouraged to eat children's favourites such as fish fingers, ice-cream and chocolate bars. They also have individual and family therapy, and the clinic has a good success rate. Dawson is clear that the problem should be nipped in the bud before it gets out of hand. The pattern commonly starts with cutting out sweets, then fatty things, then they become vegetarian. After this they switch to little more than fruit and yogurt, then diet yogurts. Then they stop eating altogether. 'It might start innocently enough,' she says. 'If a child is losing weight, they get a lot of kudos in the short term. If they refuse chocolate they are praised as strong-minded. By the time they are so thin the praise stops, the problem is out of control.'

The simple fact is that no child should ever be dieting – unless a doctor has suggested it for medical reasons – until they stop growing at around sixteen or seventeen. Parents should clamp down hard at the first sign of a problem, and insist on normal eating patterns. But the problem comes when trying to differentiate between a faddy eater and a potential anorexic. The answer to this is that faddy eaters will often refuse healthy food, but eat one particular food quite happily. The children to watch are those who cut out fat, talk about dieting, start calorie counting and turn to diet drinks to fill themselves up.

Loss of appetite can also be caused by depression, which is not uncommon in children. It can be caused by bullying, family problems, academic stress or abuse, all things which are often hidden from parents. Distress can also cause eating problems. For every one extreme case, there are hundreds which concern parents and never make it to the GP. Rhodes Farm has brought out a video guide to anorexia and bulimia for use in schools and youth groups, and Diet Breakers have begun a campaign to educate young girls and boys in normal eating patterns (see the back of the book for details of addresses and numbers).

CHAPTER 11

Eating Well and Keeping Fit

Having got this far, the next question for compulsive eaters is: how to begin eating properly again. The first problem to be overcome is to get your natural, healthy appetite back.

You could look at the way we eat, particularly in the so-called civilised world, in two different ways. First of all there is the feeling of hunger which comes from our stomachs, the messages telling us that we need to eat in order to fuel our bodies to make them operate. Here, food is the fuel we need in order to live. The second type of hunger could be described as more psychological. Everyone has felt it from time to time: you eat because there is food around, or because it's time for a meal, or because it's part of a social occasion. Most of all, you eat because you *like the idea* of eating not because you *need* it. People suffering from food disorders eat in this way, but they take it one step further and eat in response to the way they're feeling. They eat because they are sad, depressed, worried or lonely. They also eat because they are happy, excited, or simply because they feel like it.

The trouble is people suffering from eating disorders have been using food in this way for so long, they have forgotten what a normal appetite feels like and what a normal eating pattern is. If you have been keeping a diary, as we suggested in the self-help section, then look back at your eating patterns and check on which category your eating usually falls into. You will probably be surprised to find the extent to which your emotions have ruled your eating habits.

You now have to work on getting back your natural appetite and beginning to eat properly. I am not suggesting for one minute that from now on you only eat when you feel hungry and at set meal times. That is neither sensible, nor practical, because everyone eats on occasion just because they fancy what's on offer. It' s normal behaviour.

In the earlier self-help chapter we have suggested that you plan your eating and meal times to be at the easiest time for you. But you may find this is either very difficult or does not work for you. Some specialists working with people with eating disorders suggest that this strategy is abandoned altogether in favour of an eating-on-demand programme. In other words, you eat what you want, when you want. To me this seems a very difficult and unhealthy approach. After all, received wisdom tells us that we should eat three balanced meals a day.

MATCHING FOOD TO NEED

We've all heard of young children who appear to exist on nothing but two basic foodstuffs, and often two very peculiar things, such as milk and baked beans, and apparently almost nothing else. But research has shown that if left to make their choices, very young children will over the space of a short time choose all the foods they need for healthy growth and development.

What you need to do now is get in touch with your body's cravings. Sometimes you might like a salad, another time it may be steak or other meats, another time it might be potatoes or pasta or a sandwich. Again research being done in America in both humans and animals shows that if left to ourselves we tend to match the food we choose to the needs of our bodies.

Ah, but what about the fact that all you ever want to eat, especially now that you've given up dieting for ever, is a chocolate bar or a large cream cake. Many people with eating disorders have spent hours craving what are apparently highly unhealthy foods and ones which are high in calories. If you give your appetite a free rein, you will probably find that for a short time you will eat copious amounts of what you used to think of as forbidden foods. But even if you allow yourself to do that, you will get tired of them very quickly.

It's up to you to decide a course of action which suits you best. Some people feel happier to set themselves an eating programme, even if they only use it as a general guide; others might manage better with eating on demand. But major changes to your diet should be checked with your doctor first. He will also be able to give some general guidelines on a healthy diet.

Basically, choose foods which you enjoy, and vary them so that you are eating something from each of the four following groups:

- bread, breakfast cereals, rice and pasta
- fresh fruit, vegetables and potatoes
- meat, fish, eggs, pulses and nuts
- milk, cheese and yogurt

Try to make eating a pleasure and don't be tempted to grab a snack at first. Sit down with a plate, knife and fork at the table, and eat your food slowly. Don't always feel that you have to finish everything on your plate. Give yourself a short period of relaxation after your meal. It will take time for your body to adjust and you have to be prepared to put on a little weight at first and perhaps feel uncomfortable. You may also begin for the first time to find it difficult to deal with other people's food, so this is another good reason for enlisting the family's help until you feel more confident.

Fat is Important

We have been conditioned now into thinking of *fat* as an extremely bad thing. Not only do we not want to be fat, we don't want to eat it either. It's bad for us, we're told. Wrong. Fat is an essential component of any healthy diet. Not only does it make food taste better, it is a source of energy, it provides essential fatty acids and it provides and absorbs fat-soluble vitamins which our bodies need.

All over the Western world, governments have warned their citizens that they should inhibit their dietary fat in order to reduce the risk of heart disease and other illnesses. And we've heard a lot about reducing our blood cholesterol levels. Most of the work on dietary fat has been done with men, and advises that they should cut down their intake of fats rich in saturated fatty acids – those found in solid fat such as butter or lard, and in meat and dairy produce, anything of animal origin. They have been shown to increase blood cholesterol levels. But women prior to the menopause appear to have some built-in protection against heart disease, and some studies have shown that when women restrict their fat intake, there is no effect on their blood cholesterol levels, which tend to be lower than men's anyway. Yet most diet books are aimed at women and exhort them to cut down on fat.

We've already examined the problems suffered by teenagers who restrict their diets. What the diet books don't tell you very often is that the fat in butter, cheese and milk is a good source of vitamin A, that vegetable oils are a rich source of vitamin E, and that oily fish is an excellent source of vitamin D. Fat is also needed to help us *absorb* these essential vitamins, and those on low-fat diets have a very poor uptake of these vitamins. Researchers have shown that women with low intakes of vitamin A have an increased risk of breast cancer, vitamin E may offer protection against heart disease and vitamin D would help prevent osteoporosis.

We also need what are called essential fatty acids. These are found in food like nuts, vegetable oils and oily fish, yet these are just the things which many diets ban. Studies carried out by the Medical Research Council found that men who eat oil-rich fish twice a week after they have suffered a heart attack, reduce their risk of dying within two years by almost 30%.

According to Professor Vincent Marks, Professor of Clinical Biochemistry at the University of Surrey, people are being fed nutritional nonsense in many magazines and newspapers based on advice from bogus 'experts'. Writing in the journal, *Nutrition and Food Science*, Professor Marks says:

'Unfortunately there is nothing to stop anyone setting themselves up as a nutrition expert and giving advice which sounds plausible but is arrant nonsense. An understanding of nutrition requires a thorough knowledge of human biology and it can be downright dangerous to follow advice from experts who are not properly qualified to give it. Self-appointed nutritionists, usually with a vested interest or an axe to grind, are exploiting the absence of registerable qualification in human nutrition to promote their unsupported opinions as though they were scientific facts.

'The constant supply of newspaper and magazine articles promoting unproven slimming diets and the other more bizarre health claims – such as purporting to "detoxify" the system – testifies to the importance members of the public attach to information on nutrition. Readers deserve better than most of them are getting.'

So who says fat isn't good for you? The problem is that we've all listened for so long to the twisted message of the diet-pushers. Fat is essential in a healthy diet and laying down fat stores is perfectly normal. What we have got out of balance is that we don't use up as much energy as we are fuelling our bodies to provide. Where we go wrong is that we have got the exercise part of the equation all wrong.

THE ADVANTAGES OF EXERCISE

Some people think only of exercise in terms of losing weight. It can certainly contribute a little, but you would have to cycle for about sixteen hours non-stop to lose one kilo (2¼lb) of body fat. What exercise *does* do is improve muscle tone and make you look and feel better.

Exercise is good for you. It can help protect against diseases such as heart disease, osteoporosis and high blood pressure. It can help to reduce stress, it can even improve your social life. And while most people have taken on board the healthy eating message in recent years, few have responded in the same way to the exercise message.

Back in 1792, the writer William Buchan observed: '. . . it is evident from the structure of the body, that exercise is no less necessary than food for the preservation of health.' He had come to this conclusion from watching the effects of the increased use of horse-drawn carriages and sedans on the men and women who used them!

There is now a huge body of scientific evidence to show that exercise in early and middle life can be beneficial in delaying the onset or progression of some serious diseases. There is also a growing body of evidence to show that the older we get, the more vital exercise is to our general health. And what's more it's never too late to start. People who exercise regularly tend to suffer less from all sorts of general aches and pains. They have fewer headaches, less stiffness, fewer painful joints, less chronic back pain and less insomnia. A lack of activity, on the other hand, can cause all sorts of problems: poor circulation, weak muscles, stiff joints, shortness of breath, loss of bone mass, depression and a general feeling of tiredness and having no energy.

For those suffering from eating disorders, an addiction to

exercise may have become part of the problem, so you need to rethink your approach to exercise, and maybe start again from the beginning.

Before you embark on any kind of fitness programme, it's a good idea to consult your doctor, particularly if you have any kind of cardiac or respiratory complaint, if you suffer from frequent dizzy spells, high blood pressure or a bone or joint problem, or if you are taking regular medication.

Here are a few guidelines before you begin:

● Don't exercise if you are not feeling well, especially if you have had flu, a cold, a fever or any other viral infection or debilitating illness within the last couple of years.
● Don't 'go for the burn'. If it hurts, it isn't doing you any good at all. There is a world of difference between getting your muscles working and a part of your body hurting. If some part of your exercise becomes painful or does not feel right, stop at once and go back to doing something more gentle.
● Make sure you drink plenty of fluids – not alcohol – before, during and after your exercise to prevent dehydration.
● Don't exercise immediately after you have eaten. Wait for at least half an hour to give your body a chance to begin the digestive process and to avoid making yourself feel sick.
● Don't try too much, too soon. Aiming too high can lead to failure and disappointment and that is the last thing you need at this point in your recovery.

Where to Start
There is no need to go into formal exercise classes if that's not your scene. You can do just as much good on your own at home or during everyday life. Begin by spending more time

each day walking. Take the stairs rather than the lift or the escalator, or simply walk up and down stairs at home a few times. When you are sitting watching TV or doing something that requires little physical effort, begin moving by scretching your fingers and toes. Turn your ankles and wrists, slowly and rhythmically round one way and then the other. Hunch your shoulders and relax. Try moving one shoulder at a time round one way and then the other. Stretch out your arms and legs. Breathe slowly and deeply. Another simple exercise to try at home is to tighten your abdominal muscles and then relax them. Try this with your pelvic floor muscles, too. When you go to the toilet, stop yourself in mid-flow, count to five and carry on.

Women at home tend to be on the go all the time, but household chores are often activities which put a strain on our bodies, mainly our backs. To counterbalance these effects, we need a complete exercise programme that includes stretching, strengthening, correct posture, and which also makes our hearts work more efficiently. A good exercise regime will improve flexibility, muscle strength and the heart rate and will also help body composition – the ratio of body fat to lean body mass.

Exercise may be described as being aerobic or anaerobic according to its intensity. Anaerobic exercise is defined thus: the higher the intensity the more the muscles have to rely on producing energy *without oxygen* (that is, anaerobically). Typically, anaerobic exercise is of high intensity maximum exertion and of short duration (less than one minute or so) such as sprinting, jumping, heavyweight training etc. Aerobic exercise is defined thus: if exercise is of low to moderate intensity, sufficient energy can be produced *using oxygen* (that is, aerobically), and the exercise may be continued for a considerable length of time (upwards of 20 minutes or more).

Walking, jogging, cycling, swimming and other 'whole body' exercises are predominantly aerobic.

Always remember to warm up and to cool down afterwards to help prevent injuries. You can simply do a few minutes marching on the spot at the beginning and end of your programme.

For more information, contact one or more of the organisations below.

• You can send for a free leaflet of safe exercising from **The Consumers' Association**. Write to Dept AM, The Consumers' Association, 2 Marylebone Road, London NW1 4DF. Send a large SAE.

• **The Health Education Authority** and **The Sports Council** publish a booklet called **Exercise. Why Bother?** which is free. Send a SAE to HEA, Hamilton House, Mabledon Place, London WC1H 9TX.

• **The Chartered Society of Physiotherapy** publishes leaflets on safe exercise for older people. Send a large SAE to 14 Bedford Row, London WC1R 4ED.

• If you are looking for an exercise class, make sure your instructor is properly qualified and has an RSA or Sports Council Basic Certificate in the Teaching of Exercise to Music.

• **The Sports Council** has general information about sporting opportunities near you. To find your regional office, telephone 0171 388 1277.

CHAPTER 12

Learning to Like Yourself

The final step on the ladder of recovery is to learn to like yourself and accept yourself for what you are. People with eating disorders constantly wish 'if only'. We all do that at some time or another, but the preoccupation with weight and the way we look has led to the conviction that 'If only I was thin' then everything else in my life would somehow be all right. Of course, this is not the case.

We've already demonstrated that women in general seldom have a realistic view of the way they look. Standing in front of a mirror they will automatically add a few pounds to what they see. Those suffering from eating disorders distort this view of themselves even more.

You are probably much too critical of yourself. Nobody can possibly be perfect all the time. Nobody *is* perfect all the time. We all of us fail at things we attempt from time to time, and there is no disgrace in that. People with eating disorders need to know that it is OK to fail; to err is human. You may well feel at the beginning of your journey back that you are failing all the time. If you feel like this, then sit down, read back through your diary and compare this to the way things were before. You'll find that things are nowhere near as bad as they were before you decided to stop being dominated by food and weight.

I love my body just
the way it is . . .
I love my bulgy belly . . .
I love my —
oh forget it

You must also learn to take a positive view of things that happen, rather than always being negative. Whatever you do, you will be helped if you turn your way of thinking round so that you try and look at everything in a more positive light. It is in fact very much easier just to sit there and blame yourself for everything that goes wrong or feels wrong, and asking yourself 'So what's the point?' is a good excuse to give in and not bother any more.

Let's look at some examples:

Nobody likes me . . . and yet the girl who made the unkind remark about people with weight problems at work today definitely has problems of her own. None of the others took any notice and actually no one else has said anything remotely like that to me. In fact that girl in the next office said how much she liked my new skirt last week . . . .

I have no real friends . . . and whose fault is that? One of the symptoms of my eating disorder has been a total absorption with food and weight. I haven't given anyone the chance to get close to me. So, now all that's changed, what about that nice lady at the school gates who invited me back to coffee at her home, or what about that group of girls I was at school with, or the people I used to work with?

I'm never going to get over this habit of bingeing . . . I skipped lunch and after eating hardly anything for breakfast, my blood sugar level dropped really low, so it's no wonder I began to crave something sweet. I now know that missing out on meals will make me feel like this and more susceptible to a binge. I must concentrate on eating properly and not get myself into that situation again . . . .

MAKING THE BEST OF YOURSELF

You may also find it helpful as you begin to get better to boost your confidence by trying this exercise. Sit down with a blank piece of paper. Divide it into two columns and on one side write down the things which you feel are wrong, or negative, about the way you are, and then using the procedure illustrated in the examples above, turn these negatives into positive attributes. If you can't always think of a positive way of looking at something, then simply write down a list of the positive things you've done in the last week. It can include anything from helping an old lady across the road, to doing a good turn for a friend, to turning in a good piece of work at school, the possibilities are endless. Looking at things in this way will soon help you to begin to like yourself more and will also help you to begin to believe that you are likeable, too.

ASSERTIVENESS TRAINING

If you are beginning to recover but still feel very strongly that you lack self-confidence and you just don't know how to

go about building a new life, then perhaps you should think about assertiveness training. Many people who don't know much about this kind of thing tend to think it's the sort of thing that dyed-in-the-wool feminists indulge in, or successful high-flying businesswomen. Not at all. Assertiveness training can help everyone. It will give you the confidence to make your feelings and wishes known, rather than giving way to others all the time. It will also help you to learn about your own needs and wishes. In the long run it can help improve your relationship with others and it may even improve your prospects at work.

Assertiveness is not about being angry or aggressive or unpleasant, it's about giving you the strength and confidence to speak up for yourself, to help you achieve what you want in life, and to be able to say no if necessary.

You should be able to find something near you by approaching your education office for a list of adult education courses. Some courses may well be advertised in the local paper, your health-food shop or even your local health centre.

BUILDING A NEW LIFE

Most people with eating disorders, having made the decision that they want to escape the prison they have built around themselves, want an instant remedy, a miracle cure. There isn't one. Your obsession with food has probably taken years to get a hold over your life, and it is going to take time for you to escape and build a new life free of it. It's a long, painful and sometimes a lonely road back to recovery. You will have setbacks, but every time you pick yourself up and try again, it will be that bit easier the next time. You will have good days and bad days, and even on good days, you will encounter problems which you will find difficult or even impossible to deal with. But that's life, and you must remember it's the same for everyone, whether they are recovering from an eating disorder or not. When you feel you have achieved something, don't be afraid to reward yourself. And write down everything, so that on bad days you can look back to the good ones and cheer yourself up. You've made the biggest leap forward by acknowledging your problem and starting to do something about it. That on its own is something worth celebrating.

Useful Addresses

Many of the organisations listed here are run on a voluntary basis. When writing to them, please enclose a stamped, self-addressed envelope.

Eating Disorders Association
  Sackville Place,
  44 Magdalen Street,
  Norwich NR3 1JU
  Tel: Helpline for over 18s 01603 621414
      Helpline for under 18s 01603 765050

For children and teenagers:

Rhodes Farm Clinic
  The Ridgeway,
  Mill Hill,
  London NW7 1RH
  Tel: 0181 906 0885

The Priory Centre
  11 Priory Road,
  High Wycombe,
  Bucks HP13 6SL
  Tel: 01494 21431

Society for the Advancement of Research into Anorexia
Stanthorpe,
New Pound,
Wisborough Green,
Billingshurst,
West Sussex RH14 0EJ

The Women's Therapy Centre
6–9 Manor Gardens,
London N7 6LA

Overeaters Anonymous
PO Box 19,
Stretford,
Manchester M32 9EB

Diet Breakers
Church Cottage,
Barford St Michael,
Banbury,
Oxon OX15 0UA
Tel: 01869 37070

Weigh Ahead
2 The Crescent,
Busby,
Glasgow G76 8HT

The Scottish Centre for Eating Disorders
3 Sciennes Road,
Edinburgh EH9 1LE
Tel: 0131 667 8642

The Maisner Centre
   Box 464,
   Hove,
   East Sussex BN3 2BN
   Tel: 01273 729818

Further Reading

Anorexia Nervosa, a guide for sufferers and their families, R.L. Palmer, Penguin Books.

Bulimia, a guide for sufferers and their families, Dr David Haslam, Cedar Books.

Overcoming Overeating, Conquer Your Obsession with Food, Jane R. Hirschmann and Carol H. Munter, Cedar Books.

Consuming Passions, What to Do When Food Rules Your Life, Paulette Maisner with Rosemary Turner, Thorsons.

Eating your Heart Out, Julia Buckroyd, Optima.

You Don't Have to Diet, Dr Tom Sanders and Peter Bazalgette, Bantam Press.

Anorexia Nervosa and Bulimia: How to Help, Marilyn Duke and Roger Slade, The Open University Press.

The Forbidden Body, Why Being Fat is not a Sin, Shelley Bovey, Pandora.

Big is Beautiful, Challenging the Myths and Celebrating our Size, Margaret Greaves, Grafton Books.

Hunger Strike, Susie Orbach, Penguin Books.

Eating Disorders, Hilde Bruch, Routledge and Kegan Paul.

Feeding the Hungry Heart, Geneen Roth, Signet.

The Good Health Handbook, Dr Peter Mansfield, Grafton Books.

Index